The Good Retreat Guide

Stafford Whiteaker

RIDER
LONDON • SYDNEY • AUCKLAND • JOHANNESBURG

For my brothers and sisters at Turvey Abbey

Acknowledgements
Illustrations by Sr Regina Rynja O.S.B., Prior of Our Lady of Peace, Turvey Abbey.
Book design by Diana Goddard, Goddard Associates, Ludlow.
Assistance with French section Judith Adams.

First published in 1991 by Rider
An imprint of Random Century Group Ltd
20 Vauxhall Bridge Road, London SW1V 2SA

Revised edition 1994

Random House Australia (Pty) Ltd
20 Alfred Street, Milsons Point,
Sydney, NSW 2061, Australia

Random House New Zealand Ltd,
18 Poland Road, Glenfield,
Auckland 10, New Zealand

Random House South Africa (Pty) Ltd,
PO Box 337, Bergvlei 2012, South Africa

Printed and bound in Great Britain by
Mackays of Chatham PLC, Chatham, Kent

The right of Stafford Whiteaker to be identified as the author of this work has been
asserted by him in accordance with the Copyright, Designs and Patents Act, 1988.

A catalogue record of this book is available
from the British Library.

ISBN 0-7126-6047

6 **CONTENTS**

SEEKING INNER PEACE
The British increasingly search for silence and simplicity. The French 'back to nature movement' is winning converts from the middle classes. The Germans continue to seek peace in forest walks and camping out. A new kind of pilgrim who may never go to church joins the religious on the great way of Santiago de Compostela. Those who claim not to believe in God happily join monks to sing ancient psalms. All this yearning for peace has resulted in the biggest growth in retreats in Europe since it was a religious tradition of the Middle Ages. After decades of catering for the demands of our minds and bodies, the spiritual has risen to restake its claim in our well-being.

In lives filled with ever-increasing noise, confusion and threatening events beyond their control, it is not surprising that people are overwhelmed and seek some place where they may spend a few days in inner peace. They want some deep nourishment, respite and sense of haven. Ordinary holidays are hardly suitable. In response to this demand, the doors of Christian and Buddhist convents and monasteries across Europe are opening to receive guests who seek the peaceful surroundings in which a hidden world of the heart is lived out. Such hospitality and sanctuary has always been on offer. It is only that people are rediscovering it.

A JOURNEY OF DISCOVERY
For saint, sinner and ordinary folk, the spirit offers an immeasurable journey of discovery. It is the element of ourselves that unites us to all other life. It liberates us from the tyranny of the mind and the pitiful struggle of the body against time. It is the voice within us that asks for an opportunity to think things through, to get away from it all for just a little while, and to reflect on our lives and relationships. Our spiritual selves remain hungry for attention and persistently thirsty for growth. Can there ever have been a man or woman who has not asked: 'Who am I?'

The factors at play in our personal growth are exceedingly elusive. They are at once subjective feelings and emotions that at first may be seen clearly, then not at all. Lao Tse, the founder of Taoism who lived in the sixth century before Christ, said that the growth principle in life is too elusive to be named or to be grasped at all. Yet, even in this mystery of self, we can experience not only visible growth but that which is hidden. We can achieve this only by allowing our spirit to flourish.

Nothing will happen until you find some peace and quiet in a place where distractions of every kind are at a minimum. Our usual holidays can not provide this kind of sanctuary. Even a quiet day alone at home is likely to end in the performing of some long-postponed domestic task. We must withdraw from our ordinary lives. This is why going on retreat is often a good solution.

This book aims to help you find just such a place in which to begin or continue this journey of discovery.

WHAT IS A RETREAT?

A retreat is a deliberate attempt to step outside our ordinary life. It is an inward exploration that lets our feelings open out and gives us access to both the light and dark corners of our deepest feelings and relationships. When we are able to reflect upon the discoveries we have made about ourselves, we grow in personal knowledge, opening ourselves to the adventure of living and to the manifest rewards of love. For most it will be a movement away from the ego and towards peace; for many, an awakening to the presence of God in their lives.

A retreat offers a different experience for each person, whether alone or in a group. A private retreat may last from a day to many months, but most people, when they first go, find a long weekend the most suitable length of stay. Most group retreats run for periods of a day, a weekend or a week.

A retreat is not an escape from reality. Silence and stillness are a very great challenge in this age of noise, diversion and aggression. Our lives are filled with preoccupations, distractions and sound. Even after a few hours of stillness, an inner consciousness opens up within ourselves, which is an unexpected and, for many people, a rather startling experience. Modern man has difficulty with silence.

In opening up our interior self, we may find a surprising void – an empty inner space we never knew existed. Suddenly, there are no radios, televisions, friends, children, pets and the constant background of human activity. We are faced with ourselves. Then come the big questions that no one really likes to face and, yet, are the very questions that haunt our lives: 'Who am I? What am I? Where am I going? What is my life really about?' Happily, we have space and time on retreat to dwell on this awareness of our deepest fears and feelings. In these moments a retreat truly begins, for this new consciousness starts a meditation on self that is the giving of undivided attention to the spirit. Some have said that it is opening the door to God.

But it is not true that you have to be quiet all the time. Many retreats have little or no silence and there are retreat houses which can be noisy when fully booked.

In any case, if you are desperate, there will be people at hand to help you. And if the combination of silence and stillness is too much for you, you may well find that a quiet activity such as walking, sewing or painting is the best way to journey inwards. Many retreat centres offer a variety of activities.

WHO GOES ON RETREATS?

At a retreat centre you will meet people of all ages and from every kind of background – students, housewives, grandparents, businessmen and women, the rich and the poor. A group retreat can be fun. Even on a private retreat you are likely to meet interesting people.

Having placed yourself amongst strangers, you may meet people whom you like at once, those whom you are disinclined to know better and those who may make a nuisance of themselves – the kind of person who has a problem and cannot help talking about it to everyone and anyone. You may also meet another kind of person: someone who persists in hammering away about God and salvation or the greening of the planet in a manner that is apt to bore even the most virtuous retreatant. If cornered by either of these two types, don't be embarrassed about cutting it short. You are there for another purpose, so excuse yourself without hesitation and go away at once to your room or for a walk. On the other hand, you may find it both charitable and instructive to really listen to what the person is saying. The choice is yours.

DO YOU HAVE TO BE RELIGIOUS?

You do not have to be a Christian or Buddhist to go on a retreat, even if you go to a monastery. Men and women of all faiths and those of none go on retreat. The important factor is your positive decision to take this time for the nourishment and enrichment of your spiritual life. Access to places of the Islamic faith is a different matter and you must enquire first as to the opportunity. You should also enquire first at Hindu places of worship and study. The Inter-faith Network, whose address is listed in the guide under 'Helpful Addresses' will be able to assist you in these matters.

GOING ON RETREAT

If you have never been on retreat before, you will be venturing into unknown territory. Whether you choose a monastery, a convent or a meditation centre, you may well feel apprehensive about going if you are striking out on your own. How should you behave? What should you do? If you go to a monastery, everyone seems so busy – and there will be bells ringing for prayers, for meals, for work starting and stopping. It can be confusing and strange. On top of all this, you are faced on a group retreat with the possibility of having to talk about how you feel about God, about prayer and about yourself. It is a prospect that stops many people from going on retreat. But the following steps will give you a good basis for feeling comfortable about it all.

First, select a place which strikes you as interesting in an area of the country which you think would be nice to visit. Then write an introductory letter, giving the dates you would like to stay, with an alternative time, and making it clear whether you are a man or woman. Ask if you need to bring anything particular such as towels, soap or special clothing and what time of arrival would be best. Finally, ENCLOSE A STAMPED, SELF-ADDRESSED ENVELOPE. Almost all places of retreat have limited financial resources and many letters to answer, so postage is a big expense. You don't have to say anything more about yourself unless it is specified in this guide. You need not declare either your faith or lack of it, your age or circumstances. If you decide to go on a group retreat, then most places have a brochure detailing what is on offer.

When you arrive, you can expect to be welcomed and made to feel at home. Don't worry about what to do next – someone will tell you what the arrangements are for all the basics like meals and worship.

A TYPICAL DAY ON RETREAT

A simple Christian day-retreat might be as follows. You arrive at your destination – say, a convent. The sister who is the guestmistress shows you to a quiet room where you meet a few other people who form a small group. Coffee is followed by a short introduction by one of the sisters or the retreat leader telling you about the place and the day's programme. From that moment until after lunch you and the others on retreat maintain silence. There will perhaps be a morning talk followed by worship or group prayer. You are not obliged to attend these if you choose not to. At lunch, you eat in silence while someone reads aloud from a spiritual work, or you may all talk, get acquainted and exchange views. Then a walk alone through a park or into the nearby countryside, followed by a talk from the retreat leader with a group discussion, ending on a sharing of thoughts and prayer.

A typical Buddhist day-retreat may have more silence and certainly more formal meditation times. But, again, you will be sharing with others in a new and gentle way.

At a New Age centre the day may well include more active sessions and draw on the spiritual practices of Eastern or tribal cultures. If you want to have time to yourself, check in advance that there are no sound-orientated workshops in session.

OBTAINING SPIRITUAL HELP

If you need to talk to someone about your life or your problems, many retreat places offer time for personal interviews of this nature. However, such talks should lead to some spiritual benefit. Those with overriding emotional and psychological problems should seek help elsewhere unless this kind of counselling by professionally trained and qualified people is specifically offered. On the other hand, if you need to talk to someone about your spiritual life and could do with some guidance, then most places of retreat will have someone who can help you. Meditation, shared prayer, group discussions and directed reading are all ways of obtaining spiritual help.

DIFFERENT KIND OF RETREATS

Retreats are not a new phenomenon. All the world's great religions have found that men and women need at times to withdraw temporarily from daily living in order to nourish their spiritual life. Moses retreated to Mount Sinai. Jesus went into the desert. Buddhists annually make a retreat. Moslems go for a day of prayer and fasting within the mosque. The Hindu withdraws to the temple or wanders alone across the land.

Private and group retreats

Private retreats are those in which you go alone as an individual. Group retreats are for those in a group and these are usually led by someone who is experienced in such matters. The group may be from a parish or consist of a number of people from different places coming together. Group retreats often have a theme or cover a particular topic or approach to spirituality. The retreat programme of the place will explain what these are.

Silent retreats

Silent retreats are an adventure into stillness. There are some especially designed to provide you with techniques to help you lose your dependence on noise and distractions so that you are not upset the first time you experience this rare exposure to your innermost feelings.

Individually selected retreats

These are structured around a particular system of spiritual exercises, such as those of St Ignatius, or based upon a defined form of meditation such as Vipassana, one of India's most ancient forms of meditation.

Traditional weekend retreats

These are the most popular form of retreat and are likely to run along the following lines. You arrive on Friday evening, settle your things in your room and go down to meet the retreat leader and the other guests. After supper you meet for a short talk about the weekend and are given a timetable. From that time onwards you will cease talking unless it is to the retreat conductor or unless a group discussion or shared prayer is held. During Saturday and Sunday there will be religious ceremonies of some nature and probably a short address to the group on subjects which help you meditate and pray. There will be times for walks, reading and just resting. It is all simple, easy and peaceful.

Theme and activity retreats

In the last few years the growth in awareness of the intimate connection between mind, body and spirit has produced a wide range of courses and study retreats that combine physical and spiritual understanding through methods which spring from modern knowledge or which are based on rediscovering traditional forms of spiritual awakening. You enter an activity, such as painting or dance, through which you gather your feelings, senses and intuition together into a greater awareness of self, of others and of God.

There are a great number of ways to explore this form of retreat. Here are just a few that you may find on offer in retreat houses in this guide. Some are ancient arts and others very much of our own time.

Yoga retreats employ body and breathing exercises to achieve greater physical and mental stillness as an aid to meditation and contemplation.

Embroidery, calligraphy and painting retreats focus on awakening personal creativity. Through this opening of new personal horizons an awareness of others may develop, together with a sense of creation beyond one's own efforts and personal world.

Icon painting is creating a religious work of art as a form of prayer. It is an established Christian spiritual tradition, particularly in the Orthodox Church, and a very popular type of activity retreat. You do not have to be an artist to enjoy and benefit from such an experience. One of the best leaders of icon-painting retreats is Sister Esther Pollak at Turvey Abbey, Bedfordshire, where such a weekend is usually on offer in their retreat programme. Similar to this, but in the Hindu tradition, is yantra painting, offered by a number of yoga centres.

Music and dance have long been part of religious worship and the praise of God. The psalms call us to bring forth our songs, trumpets, lutes, harps, timbrels, and to dance. Don't worry if you can't sing very well or if you don't play a musical instrument or if you have never danced. That is not important. What is important are your good intentions, for music-and-dance retreats are a joyous encounter. They are apt to bring a gladness of heart that surprises and delights.

Nature and prayer retreats link care for the environment to your life and help you pray and become aware of the unity of all things in creation. Time is spent on observing flowers, birds and trees. They are active retreats, but ones in which stillness, meditation and prayer also play a part. They may well include 'awareness walks' in which you concentrate on seeing things freshly, learning to appreciate colour, shape and texture in order to heighten your awareness of creation at work all around you. This awareness of the inter-connectedness between all of creation is very much part of both Buddhist and New Age approaches to spirituality.

Gardening and prayer Most retreat houses have good gardens, and in this form of retreat some practical work is combined with the study of plants, trees and shrubs. Along with talks and time for rest and prayer, this kind of retreat works well in developing awareness of the world around you and can bring the benefit of working happily and productively with others – not something that many people today find true of their ordinary daily job.

Renewal retreats

Christian renewal means a new awareness of the presence of Christ, a deeper experience of the Holy Spirit and a clearer understanding for the committed Christian of his or her mission in the Church. If you think this kind of retreat is for you, then discuss the matter first, if you can, with your priest or minister.

Healing retreats

Inner healing and healing of the physical body through prayer and the laying-on of hands have become prominent features of many Christian ministries today. It is often a feature too of New Age gatherings and explorations. Healing may be concerned with a physical complaint or with the healing of the whole person in order to eliminate obstacles to personal and spiritual growth. It can help us realise our own potential through prayer as healers and reconcilers. For the Christian this always involves the inspirational power of the Holy Spirit.

Contemplative retreats

The aim is to be still and, through silence and intuitive prayer, to hold yourself open to God from the very core of your being. Contemplative prayer is not an intellectual exercise, yet it is demanding and searching, even painful on occasion, as the lives of numerous saints and holy men and women bear testimony. A convent or monastery devoted to a contemplative way of life is probably the best place for you if you want to make this kind of retreat. There you will find spiritual support by joining the community in their daily round of prayer and worship. Contemplation as a way of spiritual awareness is not confined to Christianity but is part of the practice of other faiths as well.

Family retreats

At those places that have suitable facilities, a whole family may experience going on retreat together. These retreats need to be well planned and worked out so that each member of the family, from the youngest to the oldest, has a real chance to benefit from the experience. It would be difficult to find any convent, monastery, or temple in which children would not be welcomed with love and joy – but many such places simply have no facilities for children. Like it or not, restless children and crying babies are a distraction for those at prayer and for anyone seeking interior stillness. So take your children to a place that clearly states they have facilities – then you can relax and so can everyone else. Buddhist centres and monasteries often have children's 'Dahampasala' which is a school study-session held each Sunday.

Drop-in retreats

These are non-residential. The idea is that you live at home or stay elsewhere and 'drop in' to take part in the resident community's regular pattern of prayer or for a series of talks and other activities planned around a set programme. This is an increasingly popular type of retreat for those who have neither time nor resources to go away or whose commitments may prevent them from being away from home overnight. The idea of a drop-in retreat is a new idea for many Christians, but friends of a Buddhist centre or monastery normally attend on such a basis.

Day retreats

The programme for a day retreat can be very flexible. It might be a day of silence, a theme or activity centred day, a time for group discussion or talks, or for lessons in meditation technique. The day retreat is rather like a mini-retreat. It allows you to explore a number of different types of retreat during the year without taking a great deal of time away.

Preached retreats

These are traditional conducted retreats which may be limited to a group from a parish or other organisation or may be open for anyone to join in. The retreat conductor may be a clerical or lay person. Sometimes such retreats are led by a team rather than one person. Usually the retreat is planned around a series of daily talks designed to inspire and to provide material for individual and group meditation and prayer. There can be opportunity for silence, but not always. Sharing together is a feature of these retreats.

'Open door' retreats

The 'open door' retreat provides help to make a retreat in your own home while having direction and the support of a group. The idea is for a trained leader or a team of two religious or lay people to go to a private house or local church where a small group wish to meet. The group comes together for a few hours each week over a number of continuous weeks. The group members make a commitment to pray individually during their days back in their own home and to hold regular prayer meetings. The leader provides guidance, materials and talks, which help all the members of the group in their meditation and reflection.

Meditation retreats

While all retreats are to a lesser or greater degree supposed to allow some time for individual meditation, there has been a growing demand for retreats specifically aimed at the study and practice of meditation. The Buddhist response to this has been excellent, creating many opportunities for learning how to meditate. In addition to weekly classes, most Buddhist centres and monasteries hold a monthly meditation retreat that is open to both beginners and the more experienced, enabling them to participate in what is considered to be an all-important practice of spirituality. In Christianity, meditation was long felt to be discursive, and the approach was to reflect in a devout way on some theme, often a biblical one. While this practice remains, there has been a worldwide revival of earlier Christian approaches to meditation which share much in common with those found in the religious traditions of the East.

'Journalling' retreats

On this kind of retreat you are introduced to the concept and practice of keeping a journal as a spiritual exercise. The idea is that, by recording your thoughts during your retreat, you are helped to relate these to your present and future life. This daily record, whether examined privately or shared in a workshop with others, draws your life into focus. The aim is to become more sensitive to the content of your life and to see the continuity of your inner self.

THE CHOICE IS YOURS

There are many kinds of retreat other than those listed above. Most aim towards self-discovery of an experiential nature. The choices grow by the year and are becoming ever more imaginative. In America, for instance, there is a swimming retreat where you join dolphins in their water world. No matter the theme or activity involved or the tradition on which the retreat is based, all of them share the aim of helping you to deepen your spiritual awareness.

THE NON-RETREATANT VISIT

'Non-retreatant' is a description often used by those running retreat houses, and the term is used in this guide. It refers to a person who is staying at a retreat centre for rest and relaxation during a short, quiet holiday and is not planning to attempt anything of a spiritual nature. Many places do not want visitors who only desire a holiday and this is understandable. Other places actively encourage this type of guest. Going on retreat has become so popular that some people do treat it as a cheap holiday, but that is hardly fair to those offering hospitality who in most cases are either poor themselves or are volunteers.

WAYS OF CHRISTIAN SPIRITUALITY

Christianity is a religious faith based on the teachings of Jesus of Nazareth who lived out his Jewish heritage. Its believers hold that Jesus is the Messiah prophesied in the Hebrew Bible. The belief of Christianity is founded on the Christian Bible, from where it developed the doctrines contained in the Creed: the Holy Trinity with God the Father as the Creator, Jesus Christ as God from God and the redeemer of humankind through his death and resurrection, and the Holy Spirit as the giver of life. All these dogmas are central to the Christian faith as practised in the various Christian communities such as the Roman Catholic, Orthodox, and the churches arising from the Reformation.

While there is a shared basic content in all Western Christian spirituality, the approaches to it may differ. For example, the approach of the 20th-century Jesuit scientist and theologian, Pierre Teilhard de Chardin, is quite different from that of the 16th-century mystic, St Teresa of Avila. Yet both belong to our common Christian heritage. Included in the many ways of Western Christian spirituality is the rich treasury of Orthodox traditions on which we may draw.

The use of a particular spiritual approach in the form of exercises or meditations is common. There are also a number of popular techniques for discovering which form of spirituality might best suit your type of personality. Spiritual exercises are methods for spiritual growth. No matter how demanding, they are designed to help bring a change of heart. They are no shortcut to sanctity, as many a nun and monk has found out. No matter what form they take, spiritual practices are essentially to be pursued in a spirit of prayer rather than as an intellectual exercise.

Today such practices have come to mean every form of examination of conscience, meditation, contemplation and vocal and mental prayer. Such activities are designed to make the spirit – rather like the body in physical training – become ready and able to get rid of flab. In this way, the spirit may become open to love and to the discovery of God's will. Some religious traditions might say it is the bringing to consciousness of the unity of all creation and of the eternal. These are ambitious tasks – but then, why not? Unlike the mind and body, the spirit goes forth with unlimited prospects.

Listed below are some ways of Christian spirituality that you are likely to find widely available in retreat programmes. There are many approaches to spirituality, including the traditions of Anglican, English, Franciscan, Augustinian, Dominican and Benedictine, to name but a few. Some, such as Black spirituality and those from the Orthodox tradition, may be less familiar. The Charismatic Movement and Pentecostalism continue to foster a reawakening of the spirituality of the early Church and their approach is becoming increasingly popular. Most people find, after a while, a particular way that seems to suit them.

St Ignatius of Loyola retreats

These are based on the spiritual exercises originated by the founder of the Jesuits, St Ignatius, in the 16th century. A full retreat can last 30 days but shorter versions are available. The retreat director who is assigned to you and works with you on a one-to-one basis, provides different material from the Gospels for daily contemplative meditation. You then have an opportunity to discuss what response this has provoked within you. In the course of the retreat, you are led with some vigour to review your life in the light of Gospel teachings and to seek God's guidance for your future. Ignatian spirituality has been described as 'finding God in all things'. It is a way of spirituality that is designed for anyone, whether Christian or pagan. The satisfaction of these exercises is found not in knowledge of the Gospels but in greater understanding of the most intimate truths of self and God.

Teresian Spirituality

St Teresa of Avila (1515–82) wrote *The Interior Castle* in order to lead individuals from the beginnings of spiritual growth to the heights of mysticism. The steps she describes in this work constitute Teresian spirituality. These steps are viewed as mansions and we progress in our spiritual pilgrimage from one to the next. The seven mansions are those of self-knowledge, detachment, humility and aridity, affective prayer, the beginning of our union with God, the mystical experience or the prayer of quiet, and, finally, the last mansion of peaceful union with God. Teresian spirituality is, at once, both logical and mystical.

Chardinian Spirituality

Pierre Teilhard de Chardin (1881–1955) did not try to present an ordered way to spiritual progress although he was a Jesuit and follower of St Ignatius. Chardinian spirituality confronts the question of how to be in the world but not of it. It has a cosmic focus which eventually leads to man's love of the world coinciding with his love for Christ. In order to do this, we reconcile a love of God with a love of the world but detach ourselves from all that impedes spiritual growth. We may then strive towards a unified self which is real and true. From there, we are able to move in a state of love to serving others, widening the circle of this encounter with others, until we hold a cosmic view of everything. Thus, we are unified totally in Christ. It is a spirituality which is difficult for many. Yet it answers the problem, especially for modern man, of the contrast and conflict between action in the world and prayer to God.

Salesian Spirituality

Francis de Sales (1567–1622) believed that a person need not enter a convent or monastery to develop a deep spirituality. In his famous work *Introduction to the Devout Life*, he suggested five steps for spiritual growth. These make a progression from a desire for holiness through the practice of virtue to methods for spiritual renewal. His methods are gentle and have always enjoyed wide appeal among people living ordinary lives.

Celtic Spirituality

Recently there has been an emergence of retreats based on Celtic spirituality. The outstanding feature of this ancient Christian spiritual heritage is the overwhelming sense of the presence of God in the natural world. Rich in poems and songs, Celtic spirituality can bring an understanding of the depth of God's presence in his own creation. It is an ancient inheritance of Christian spirituality which has become newly appropriate in a time when we are concerned for the environment and the future of our planet.

PRAYER

Each faith has its own tradition of prayer. The Christian prayer, the 'Our Father', and the opening prayer of the Koran, when God is praised and His guidance sought on the 'Straight Path' are examples of an outstanding and important single prayer to which all may turn. The number of books about prayer and the manuals on how to pray are legion. They burden the shelves of libraries and religious institutions. Yet the question remains for most men and women: 'How should I pray?'

If there were a single way to begin, then perhaps the best might be the request: 'Grant me a pure heart'. This involves surrender of self, offering your vulnerability and patience up to God. A pure heart brings forth charity, hope, trust, faith and reconciliation. Here, love may be discovered and we may hold fast to that which is best in ourselves and in others. Perfect love is not possible since we are humans and, therefore, fallible. But a pure and willing heart, prepared to view all things through love, is constantly possible for anyone. We might fail from time to time to hold ourselves in this state because we are so human, yet it returns and we can go on again.

For those who have faith in God, divine love secretly informs the heart. Such faith makes prayer more instinctive than intellectual, and this prompting of the spirit may occur at any time and in any place. For the Christian, God is both the instigator and the object of such prayer.

MATCHING PERSONALITY TO SPIRITUALITY

Two popular techniques widely available to discover which spirituality may best suit you are the 'Enneagram' and the 'Myers-Briggs' methods.

The Enneagram

The Enneagram technique is intended to help you see yourself in the mirror of your mind, especially images of your personality that have become distorted by your basic attitudes to yourself. The Enneagram has a long history. It is reputed to have originated in Afghanistan some 200 years ago or perhaps in the early years of Christian influence in Persia. It then moved to the Indian subcontinent where it remained an oral tradition known to Sufi masters. Representing a journey into self, the purpose of the Enneagram is self-enlightenment. According to this system, there are nine types of human personality. These have a basic compulsion to behave in a certain way and this behaviour is maintained through a defence mechanism that avoids any change. For example, there are personality types who avoid at all cost anger or failure or weakness or conflict. The Enneagram technique leads to self-criticism which, in turn, leads to self-discovery. From there, we may gain a freedom from self which may open the way to deeper faith. Advocates of this spiritual exercise believe its careful study results in a new self-understanding and provides practical guidelines for healing.

Myers-Briggs

Isabel Myers-Briggs spent 40 years investigating personality types, building upon the research into personality done by Carl Jung. She set out eight qualities or characteristics found in each person. Myers-Briggs believed there were 16 personality types, all of which are either introverted or extroverted, and either perceiving or judging. By discovering which Myers-Briggs personality type you are, you select the form of spirituality which best suits you. The idea is that some personalities respond better and more easily to one way of spirituality than another. Here are a few examples. An intuitive personality might do better with a spirituality of hope. A person who is a thinking personality might do better with a spirituality centred on reason. The Myers-Briggs technique, like the Enneagram, is enjoying much popularity at the moment and a number of retreat centres offer it.

WHAT HAPPENS IN A MONASTERY?

The daily routine is different for monks and nuns who lead an active life such as teaching or nursing and for those who lead a contemplative life devoted to prayer and worship. Most people who have never stayed in a convent or monastery are afraid that somehow they will feel awkward and uncomfortable. Indeed, in a monastery or convent you *will* be sharing a different lifestyle. But once you understand the daily routine and discover that the oddly robed people around you are also ordinary men and women, then you will start to relax. As a guest, you may expect to be received with warmth and affection. Everyone will try to make you feel comfortable as quickly as possible.

Buddhist monasteries are usually places of training for monks and nuns although they often welcome guests. They traditionally are dependent on the generosity of their friends and visitors for all their material requirements, including food, so such places are kept as simple as possible.

Many Christian monasteries belong to 'enclosed' orders, like that of the Carmel Sisters. This means that the community members remain in their monastery separate from the world. There is usually a parlour in which you may meet the nuns from time to time, but you will not mix with them.

Monasteries are busy places with a day divided by prayer and work. So if you have never been to such a place, do not expect to see the monks and nuns sitting around looking holy or otherwise, for they follow an active and tough daily routine. Having said that, you are likely to be able to find someone for a little chat and, even when silence reigns, the atmosphere is a cheerful one.

Within the monastery the basics of life are in most ways like those of the outside world. Monks and nuns must eat and sleep. They have emotional ups and downs like all of us. There are health complaints and moans about changes that take place. The religious life is supposed to make you more human, not less, and even saints have been assailed with doubts. One of the most famous modern monks, Thomas Merton, expressed anxieties about his life in community until the end of his days. The famous priest-poet Gerard Manley Hopkins was never quite settled and happy. Yet no one could doubt the great personal spirituality of these men. So remember that monks and nuns are just as human as you are and that, like you, they too are seeking God.

If you stay in a guest house, you will be awakened when you wish to get up, and if you do not feel like attending any of the daily round of prayer or meditation, no one is likely to demand that you do so. However, by joining the daily rhythm of prayer and worship, you should find that it helps enormously to sustain and nourish you during your time there. If you stay inside a convent or monastery, be prepared for the bells. These let you know when it is time to pray or work or do whatever is next on the schedule. Christian monasteries, especially the contemplative ones, most often structure their life around what is called the Divine Office. The exact form may differ between, say, the

Roman Catholics and the Anglicans, but it is centered on the psalms from the bible. While this may be done in private prayer, it is usually sung by the monastic community together at designated hours of the day and night.

WAYS OF THE BUDDHA

The aim of Buddhism is to show us how to develop our capacity for awareness, love and energy to the point where we become 'enlightened' or fully awake to reality. Indeed, the word Buddha means 'One who is awake'. Although Buddhists do not believe in a supreme creator, since they believe that the world rises and declines in an eternal and timeless cycle, Buddhist philosophy still has worship which is central to its practice like all the major religions. There is a liturgy and scriptures that are chanted, physical acts of reverence, and inner worship of contemplating the Buddha which is often compared to contemplative Christian prayer.

Buddhism began in India some 2,500 years ago and its teachings spread throughout Asia. There is no doctrine and no need to hold to any particular beliefs. It offers a practical path for a deeper understanding of your life. There are many different groups in Buddhism. The two major ones are called 'Theravada' and 'Mahayana'. When you receive literature from a Buddhist centre, it will probably state which one is followed. The Theravada doctrine prevails in South-east Asia, including Sri Lanka, Burma, Thailand, Kampuchea and Laos. Mahayana doctrine predominates further north in China, Tibet, Korea, Japan and Vietnam. There are sects and schools even within these two major divisions so, in a sense, it is similar to Christianity in having many different groups and divisions around the world. Yet all spring from a single spiritual inspiration.

Much of the current interest in the West in Buddhism is due to its being non-exclusive and non-dogmatic. To be a Buddhist does not mean you have to wear strange robes or adopt Eastern customs or reject the cultural background of the West. Buddhism is often called 'a way of harmony', for the Buddha's teaching offers a set of tools to find inner peace and harmony by working with your own feelings and experience of life. By learning to look closely and honestly at your thoughts, emotions and physical feelings, you come to a new perspective for understanding your frustrations and discontent. Then, you can start to deal effectively with them. From such insights you may develop a joyful, kind and thoughtful attitude to others and to yourself. This is supposed to lead onwards to a state of love and peace. This inner examination and insight is a direct method of transforming consciousness and is termed meditation.

WHAT IS MEDITATION?

Meditation is a stillness of body and a stillness of mind. There are many different meditation techniques to help you attain this state of being. They range from Insight or Vipassana Meditation practice, from the Buddhist tradition, to Christian meditation such as that set out by the monk Dom John Main (1926–82), which now enjoys a worldwide following among Christians.

Meditation begins by relaxing the body into a state of stillness, then the mind into inner silence. Many of the techniques that achieve this start with a deliberate breathing pattern. (It is claimed that the breath is a bridge from the known to the unknown.). Such an approach is widely employed to marshal the body and mind and is used as well in yoga and the oriental practices of T'ai Ch'i and Shiatsu.

A single word or a phrase, sometimes called a 'mantra', is often used to help the regularity of your breathing. For example, in John Main's approach to meditation, the word 'Maranatha' is repeated in a slow and rhythmical fashion. This word means 'Come, Lord' in Aramaic, the language Jesus himself spoke, and is used by both St Paul and St John to conclude their writings.

Many people, even Christians, believe meditation is some strange state in which they will somehow lose control of themselves. Nothing could be further from the truth, for the aim of meditation is not concerned with thinking but with being. In such a state of consciousness, you are at peace – a peace which would not exist if you felt insecure. Millions of men and women of all faiths, and those of none, have found in meditation a method of reaching through deep, inner silence to an experience of self that leads to a more loving response to life.

THE NEW AGE APPROACH

It is easier to describe the New Age movement than to define it but, as a collection of all manner of ideas and practices, it aims at personal growth. What is included at New Age centres ranges from past-life therapy, environmental concern, telepathy, healing and animism, to the incorporation of elements from Eastern religions. For many New Age followers it is simply a way forward to self-discovery, self-help and the realisation of personal growth. The majority of the New Age ideas, techniques and approaches spring from well-established traditions of healing and self-discovery. As time passes the expression 'New Age' is becoming old-fashioned, because alternative approaches to health, healing, and self-discovery are increasingly part of every-day living.

The New Age is a diffuse cult which embraces a wide range of thinking and includes the work of prominent scientists whose discoveries – particularly in such disciplines as subatomic physics, psychology, parapsychology and geology – bring a new validity to the ancient teachings of Eastern spiritual traditions. The New Age movement has no established dogma or leaders and is very much a phenomenon of our time. Some Christians may wish to make certain before attending a New Age centre that the course or ideas put forward are not in conflict with their religious beliefs. New Age places do offer an approach to self-growth that is helpful to many people who do not want to enter an established way as offered by, say, Buddhism or Christianity. The aspect of New Age that appeals to most people is the great emphasis placed on a holistic approach, treating mind, body and spirit as inseparable. This approach is hardly new, as it is part of all the major faiths, and it is probably fair to say that the New Age draws on some of the most ancient healing traditions in the world.

The criterion for including New Age places of retreat in this guide has been that their approach is holistic, genuinely interested in helping people, fairly wide in scope and includes traditional spirituality of long standing, for example that of the North American Indians. New Age centres do not share a common central basis of belief like established religious places, so you will find each New Age place different from the other. Most centres have very active workshop programmes and will be happy to provide details. You may also find there is much talking and discussion. If you want silence then ask if that is a feature of the programme before you book.

WHAT IS YOGA?

One of the most significant developments in European spirituality, especially Britain, over the past few years has been the rapid and wide-spread popularity of yoga. From local adult education classes in village halls to centres and organisations devoted exclusively to yoga, this traditional way to stillness, spiritual openess and better health has been adopted by people of all ages and from all walks of life.

Yoga is one of the six main schools of Hinduism and the yoga philosophy regards both spirit and matter as real and traces the whole of the physical universe to a single source. In modern practice, especially in the West, some elements of yoga are emphasized more than others. For example, Hatha Yoga which is concerned with physical aspects, particularly with exercises and breathing, is often taught as a complete system of self-improvement. The calm and deliberate movements in yoga can lend themselves to deep relaxation and a peaceful harmony between mind and body. This can become a framework for prayer.

In addition to the Yoga Centres listed here, you will find that many places of retreat incorporate yoga in their programmes for spiritual development.

HOW THE GUIDE IS ORGANISED

The guide is divided into sections: England, Wales, Scotland, Northern Ireland, the Republic of Ireland, Yoga Centres, France, and Spain. Those sections covering Great Britain and Ireland are then sub-divided according to geographical region of the country. For example, South-east England. In that region you will find the county and after it the name of the city, town or village where the retreat centre is located.

After the name, address and telephone number of the retreat centre, the guide specifies the tradition to which it attaches. In the majority of cases, a short description will follow which tells you something about the place. After that, detailed information is given. When it is open and to whom. The number and kinds of rooms. Are children welcomed and is it possible to stay if you are disabled. What facilities are on offer and if any spiritual help is provided. Where you can and cannot go in the house, monastery or grounds. What kind of meals are served and whether or not vegetarians and special diets can be catered for. What special activities are available and where it is situated. How long you may stay. Finally, how to book, what the charges are and how to get there. Many places can send you a brochure or a programme of their activities and courses.

For France, the listing is by department with its number and then by city, town or village. For Spain, the listing is by place. Yoga Centres are listed by counties for Britain.

Those places which it is felt can be **highly recommended** are marked with a star symbol.

London

Brahma Kumaris World Spiritual University
Global Co-operation House
65 Pound Lane
London NW10 2HH   Telephone: 081-459 1400

Non-religious

Founded in 1937 in Karachi, the Brahma Kumaris University opened
a centre in London in the 1970's. Today there are 3,000 centres in 62
countries. It is a non-governmental organisation affiliated to the
United Nations Department of Public Information and the recipient of
seven UN Peace Messenger Awards. At each centre, courses, workshops, seminars and conferences covering a wide range of topics
including self-development, co-operative and communication skills
and meditation are on offer. Activities are held at all levels of the
community to help people cope more positively with everyday living
and to find greater harmony within themselves and their relationships.
All courses, events and activities are free of charge. In 1993, the
University opened the World Global Retreat Centre at Nuneham
Courtney near Oxford (see Oxfordshire entry). A brochure of events
and courses is available from both centres.

The Buddhapadipa Temple
14 Calonne Road
Wimbledon
London SW19 7NR   Telephone: 081-946 1357

Buddhist (Theravada)

This active Buddhist temple has up to eleven monks in community.
On offer are three forms of study and meditation retreat. Classes are
held at weekends and on two weekdays. They cover a variety of
subjects, from walking and sitting meditation, Buddhist study for
beginners, Abhidhamma study, to a Buddhist school for children.
Non-residential meditation retreats are held on one Saturday each
month, and residential ones are held three times a year, usually
of four days' duration. There are meditation classes four nights
each week and, unusually, a correspondence course in basic Buddhism.

Open: *All year. Receives men, women, young people, children.*
Rooms: *The temple has no facilities for guests but arrangements are
made for retreatants elsewhere.*
Facilities: *Shrine room, study room.*

Spiritual Help: *One-day retreats, personal talks, meditation, directed study.*
Guests Admitted to: *Temple and unrestricted access, except to private quarters.*
Meals: *Everyone eats together. Plain vegetarian food only.*
Special Activities: *Send for brochure.*
Situation: *Quiet, in town.*
Maximum Stay: *For duration of study/meditation period, class or course.*
Bookings: *By letter.*
Charges: *£30 per week inclusive*
Access: *London Underground and bus (regular service).*

Campion House
112 Thornbury Road
Isleworth
London TW7 4NN   Telephone: 081-560 1924

Roman Catholic

Campion House is situated in spacious grounds just outside London. It is a college for Roman Catholic men who have late vocations to the priesthood or who do not have the necessary academic background to enter a major seminary. It is usually possible to arrange a private retreat, and the organised programme of retreats includes one for younger people from 20 years old to their early 30s. Most of the retreats last for six days but can be shorter or longer depending on circumstances, as they are all individually guided.

Open: *All year except Easter and Christmas holidays. Receives men, women, groups, and religious.*
Rooms: *305 singles, 4 doubles.*
Facilities: *Disabled, conferences, park, garden, guest lounge and pay phone.*
Spiritual Help: *Personal talks, group sharing and meditation.*
Guests Admitted to: *Chapel.*
Meals: *Everyone eats together. Traditional food with provision for vegetarian and special diets.*
Special Activities: *Varied programme of events, including retreats and workshops. Send for brochure.*
Situation: *Close to Central London and Heathrow Airport with a large park and nearby banks and shops. They claim it is 'pitched between Heaven and Charing Cross'.*

Maximum Stay: *8 days.*
Bookings: *By letter.*
Charges: *£20 per day full board.*
Access: *London Underground or by car.*

The Centre for Creation Spirituality
St. James's Church
197 Piccadilly
London W1V 9LF   Telephone: 071 287 2741

Christian

The Creation-centered spiritual tradition, named such about fifteen years ago by a Roman Catholic priest, Matthew Fox, is present within all of the major world's religions. This tradition begins in the concept of life and earth as an 'original blessing'. Creation spirituality finds support in the writings and life of some of the most distinguished religious thinkers and mystics over the last thousand years including Hildegard of Bingen, Meister Eckhart, Julian of Norwich, and St. Francis. The Creation Spirituality movement is closely linked to ecological concerns and to a holistic view of living. Matthew Fox has written a number of books which have had a significant influence. These include *Original Blessing* and *The Coming of the Cosmic Christ*. A brochure and programme are available from the Centre.

Christian Meditation Centre
29 Campden Hill
London W8 7DX   Telephone: 071-937 0014

Interdenominational

The Centre is a focal point for the development of Christian medita-tion in the United Kingdom. It employs a method of meditation that is inspired by the work of Dom John Main (1926-82), who first learned to meditate while serving in Malaya. As a Benedictine monk, he later founded the Priory of Montreal, which has become a world-wide centre for the development of Christian meditation. While the Centre is an excellent place at which to learn a form of prayer that goes back to the desert fathers of the fourth century AD, many groups that meet throughout the country use Main techniques and the Centre can probably tell you which of the groups is the one closest to you. There are no special requirements for beginners and you will be helped to feel relaxed and comfortable when you first learn this very popular form of meditation.

Open: *All year, except B&B only in August. Receives men, women, young people and non-retreatants.*
Rooms: *3 singles.*
Facilities: *Garden, park, library, guest lounge, TV and guest telephone. There are many stairs in the house, which can be a problem for the elderly and the disabled.*
Spiritual Help: *Personal talks, meditation. Tapes of Dom John Main's teaching available, in addition to a video on meditation.*
Guests Admitted to: *Unrestricted access to all areas, including meditation room, and to work of the community.*
Meals: *Everyone eats together. Traditional food, with provision for vegetarian and special diets.*
Special Activities: *Meditation as a community three times a day, preceded by the Divine Office, and guests can join in. There are also teaching groups during some week days. Send for information.*
Situation: *In the city.*
Maximum Stay: *7 days, with some exceptions.*
Bookings: *By telephone or letter.*
Charges: *£25 per person per day and £18 B&B.*
Access: *High St Kensington Underground (Circle, District Lines). Buses: Nos. 9, 10, 27, 28, 33, 49, 52, 52A. Car: not recommended as parking difficult.*

Community of the Resurrection of Our Lord
St Peter's Bourne
40 Oakleigh Park South
London N20 9JN   Telephone: 081-445 5535

Anglican

A nice warm old-fashioned house, situated in a pleasant part of North London. One of the sisters is available on request for individually guided retreats, and the Community tries to create an atmosphere that allows guests to get some physical rest and really feel that they have escaped from the cares of ordinary daily life.

Open: *All year except August. Receives men, women, young people, groups and non-retreatants.*
Rooms: *5 singles, 3 doubles, hermitage, flat.*

Facilities: *Garden, library, guest lounge, TV and guest telephone.*
Spiritual Help: *Personal talks, meditation, directed study.*
Guests Admitted to: *Chapel. Unrestricted access.*
Meals: *Taken in guesthouse. Traditional food, with provision for vegetarians.*
Special Activities: *None, but enquire if any retreats are planned during the year.*
Situation: *Quiet, in North London, green-belt countryside within easy reach.*
Maximum Stay: *7-10 days.*
Bookings: *By telephone or letter.*
Charges: *By arrangement.*
Access: *London Underground to Totteridge, BR to Oakleigh Park.*

Damascus House Retreat & Conference Centre
The Ridgeway
Mill Hill
London NW7 1HH   Telephone: 081-959 8971

Roman Catholic – Ecumenical

The Vincentian Fathers, the Daughters of Charity and a lay retreat team are the forces that operate this very large centre. In spite of its size and potential number of guests, there is a warm and friendly atmosphere. Retreats for those seeking personal growth, for one-parent families, and for recovering alcoholics and their families are part of the Damascus House attempt to open a way forward for those who may need special help.

Open: *All year except for a few days over Christmas. Receives all.*
Rooms: *50 singles, 12 doubles; annexe with 12 singles, 8 doubles.*
Facilities: *Disabled (but no ramp or lift), conferences, 2 chapels, garden, library, guest lounge, TV and pay phone. Children are welcome, but please enquire first; no pets.*
Spiritual Help: *Personal talks by arrangement, group sharing, and meditation. Individually directed retreats and special retreat programmes for the disadvantaged. The facilities are open to self-help groups.*
Guests Admitted to: *Unrestricted access.*
Meals: *Everyone eats together. There is an outside catering firm so a wide choice of dishes is on offer and provision can be made for both vegetarians and special diets.*
Special Activities: *Extensive planned programme – tries to provide*

seminars for personal growth, parish work and counselling. Send for brochure.
Situation: *North suburbs of London. Only one hour from centre but on edge of green belt, so countryside is immediately to hand, with sheep and goats grazing on the adjacent Totteridge Common.*
Maximum Stay: *Usually a week but special arrangements can be made.*
Bookings: *By telephone or letter.*
Charges: *Retreats £27.50 per person per 24 hours, conferences £34.50 per 24 hours. Special rate arrangements are possible, so please ask.*
Access: *Mill Hill Underground, Bus No. 240 from Edgware and Golders Green Underground stations.*

Eagle's Wing Centre for Contemporary Shamanism
58 Westbere Road
London NW2 3RU   Telephone: 071-435 8174

North American Indian Spirituality – New Age

A shaman is a 'master of ecstasy', in touch with the realm of experience or reality that exists outside the limited, narrow state of our normal waking consciousness. He is also a healer, visionary, artist, and someone who can change consciousness to bring about a greater state of wholeness. Native Americans say that we are all dreamers and that there is both a collective dream of all humanity and a personal one. Chanting, drumming, dancing, instruction in the use of the medicine wheel, ceremony and celebration are all part of the Centre's teaching. While there is only day-time accommodation at the Centre, there are a number of interesting day courses and workshops which explore these traditions of spirituality. Residential courses, including weekends, are run as well as a one year course. These are held at various venues around the country.

Open: *According to programme. Receives men and women.*
Rooms: *Day accommodation only.*
Special Activities: *Send for brochure.*
Bookings: *By telephone or letter.*
Charges: *See brochure.*
Access: *London Underground and local bus.*

Ealing Abbey
Charlbury Grove
Ealing
London W5 2DY   Telephone: 081-998 2158

Roman Catholic – Inter-faith

The monks serve a large parish and there are schools attached to the Abbey, so this is a busy place, well and truly integrated into the world at large. Yet guests are welcome to share in the liturgy and community prayer, which help sustain all the various activities of the Abbey. The retreat programme is an exciting one. It includes a 'monastic experience' weekend, reflections on justice and peace, and a study of Eastern and Western approaches to mysticism. Individually guided retreats lasting a weekend, a few days or a full eight days are available, as well as preached retreats.

Open: *All year except last 2 weeks of July and the whole of August. Both men and women are received in the retreat house but no women are permitted in the monastery.*
Rooms: *7 singles, 2 doubles.*
Facilities: *Chapel, lounge.*
Spiritual Help: *Personal talks, guided retreats, spiritual guidance.*
Guests Admitted to: *Liturgy and community prayer.*
Meals: *Meals eaten in the guest house. Traditional food, vegetarian and special diets can be catered for.*
Special Activities: *Planned programme of events and regular retreats. Send for brochure.*
Situation: *Quiet but in the middle of busy Ealing.*
Maximum Stay: *By arrangement.*
Bookings: *By letter.*
Charges: *Depends on event and length of stay.*
Access: *BR: Ealing Broadway station 1 mile away. Bus: No. E2 from Ealing Broadway station to Greenford, alight at Marchwood Crescent.*

The London Buddhist Centre
51 Roman Road
London E2 0HU   Telephone: 081-981 1225

Buddhist

The Friends of the Western Buddhist Order strive to put Buddhism's essential teachings into practice in the West – the London Buddhist Centre is part of that worldwide movement. The purpose of the Centre is to teach meditation and other Buddhist practices and to provide information.

Open: *All year. Receives everyone, but is non-residential.*
Facilities: *Shrine room, information service.*
Spiritual Help: *The Centre is open for personal meditation and for enquiries about Buddhism. The atmosphere is helpful and friendly.*
Access: *London Underground Bethnal Green. Buses: Nos. 253 and 8.*

London Buddhist Vihara
5 Heathfield Gardens
Chiswick
London W4 4JU   Telephone: 081-995 9493

Buddhist

There are six monks resident at the Theravada Buddhism Centre and the Vihara is open every day from 9am to 9pm. Evening classes explore a wide range of subjects: Bhavana (meditation) instruction and practice, Beginner's Buddhism, Dhamma study, Buddhist psychology, the Sinhala language and Pali, which is the language of the Buddhist Canon. A Buddhist discussion group meets twice a month in an informal atmosphere. There are monthly retreats and a children's Sunday school. In conjunction with London University, there is a two-year curriculum giving students an intensive insight into Buddhism. The Vihara also caters for the needs of expatriate Buddhists from Asia – mainly Sri Lanka.

Open: *All year, except August. Receives everyone.*
Rooms: *Only for monks at this time, due to lack of space.*
Facilities: *Conferences, shrine room, garden, excellent library, sitting area provided for guests, pay phone, bookstall, lecture hall. Children welcomed.*

Spiritual Help: *Personal talks, meditation, directed study. Once-a-month day retreats from 2-8 pm of sitting and walking meditation.*
Guests Admitted to: *Everywhere except monks' rooms. Private meditation room and shrine room.*
Meals: *Traditional Sri Lankan food – monks eat separately, every-one else together. Vegetarians are catered for to the extent that vegetables are served separately.*
Special Activities: *See programme.*
Situation: *Quiet in the house.*
Maximum Stay: *One day.*
Bookings: *By telephone or letter.*
Charges: *By donation, but only if inclined. Charges made for university courses.*
Access: *London Underground or bus.*

Marie Reparatrice Retreat Centre
115 Ridgway
Wimbledon
London SW19 4RB   Telephone: 081-946 1088

Roman Catholic

A resident team of sisters, whose main purpose is retreat work and whose spirituality is Ignatian, run this purpose-built centre. They are available for counselling and spiritual help and offer a small but very interesting annual programme of retreats and events. In the past these have included Sioux Indian spirituality and how it is in tune with the Scriptures and reveals the invisible God through aspects of creation and through contemplative prayer.

Open: *All year except first 2 weeks July, and Christmas. Receives men, women and groups for retreat only.*
Rooms: *29 singles, including a limited number of ground-floor rooms. Bring towels and soap.*
Facilities: *Conferences, garden, library, guest lounge, pay phone, Bibles in each guest room.*
Spiritual Help: *Personal talks, group sharing, meditation and directed study retreats.*
Guests Admitted to: *Chapel and all retreat-house facilities, but not to community quarters.*
Meals: *Taken in the retreat house. Wholefood with provision for vegetarian and special diets.*
Special Activities: *Planned programme of events. Send for brochure.*

Situation: *This is a modern, purpose-built centre situated in town, but it is very quiet in the house and close to Wimbledon Common and parks.*
Maximum Stay: *8 days.*
Bookings: *Telephone enquiries, confirmation by letter.*
Charges: *May vary, so ask in advance.*
Access: *BR to Wimbledon from Waterloo. Underground: District Line for Wimbledon. Bus No. 200 or taxi from BR station. See brochure for car route.*

The National Retreat Association
Liddon House
24 South Audley Street
London S1Y 5DL   Telephone: 071-493 3534

Christian - Ecumenical

The National Retreat Association is an ecumenical federation of six retreat groups - the Association for Promoting Retreats (mainly Anglican), the National Retreat Movement (mainly Roman Catholic), the Methodist Retreat Group, the Baptist Union Retreat Group, the United Reformed Church Silence and Retreat Group, and the Quaker Retreats and One-to-One Ministry. It aims to foster and develop the rich and diverse expression of Christian spirituality. The Association provides information and resources about retreats, promotes the work of retreat houses, co-ordinates information about training courses in spirituality and spiritual direction, and publishes an annual journal, *The Vision,* which lists retreat houses and their programmes in Britain and Ireland. There are articles about retreats and the journal is available by post from the Association or from some Christian bookshops. Various other publications are available. Send SAE for list.

Open: *For information, see above.*
Access: *Buses: Nos. 10, 16, 26, 36, 73, 135, 137. London Underground: Bond Street or Green Park.*

'Prayer is a matter of being more aware, of being more ready still to lift up one's heart' – Dom Edmund Jones

Priory of Christ the King
Bramley Road
London N14 4HE   Telephone: 081-440 7769

Roman Catholic, but open to all

The Priory provides a relaxing atmosphere where guests can come for
a little 'space' among a small group of Benedictine monks whose main
work is pastoral care. The guest house is in its own garden, adjacent
to the church where the monks conduct the Divine Office and Mass
three times a day. They are able to converse with guests in French,
Italian, German, Dutch and Spanish. There is a healing ministry for
the sick, available to anyone, in which a group comes and ministers
three times a week, offering prayer and the laying on of hands. One
of the monks, Brother Benedict Heron has written a clear and
informative book, *Praying for Healing: The Challenge,* which ex-
plores the subject of Christian healing. It is full of practical wisdom
and gives examples of testimonies to the healing power of prayer.

Open: *All year. Receives men, women, young people under super-*
vision, families, groups and non-retreatants.
Rooms: *6 singles and a hermitage.*
Facilities: *Disabled, conferences for up to 30 day-visitors, garden,*
nearby park, library, guest lounge and guest telephone.
Spiritual Help: *Personal talks, group sharing, meditation (teachings*
of Dom Main), directed study. An Ecumenical Charismatic Prayer
Group meets in the church once a week.
Guests Admitted to: *Chapel, choir, and may help in the garden or*
with light household duties in the guest house. Guests are not usually
admitted to the monastery enclosure.
Meals: *Self-catering. Enquire about what is provided and what you*
need to bring yourself.
Special Activities: *There are activities available but everything is*
optional. All guests are free to come and go as they please.
Situation: *On the edge of a North London suburb, with walks nearby*
and opposite a large country park in the green belt. Usually quiet but
can be rather busy, especially in summer.
Maximum Stay: *Two weeks.*
Bookings: *By letter.*
Charges: *£12 B&B.*
Access: *Piccadilly Line to Oakwood. Car route M25 exit 24, A111.*

Royal Foundation of St Katherine
2 Butchers Row
London E14 8DS   Telephone: 071-790 3540

Anglican

The St Katherine community of men and women serves people living in the area through teaching, spiritual ministry and social work. The retreat and conference programmes are wide-ranging and interesting. For example, there are sessions on Zen Christian Practice, seeking to discover a way which can strengthen personal spiritual practice and at the same time help to unite two major spiritual traditions of East and West. There is a range of weekend retreats and courses on offer from music-making and drawing to those for lesbian and gay Christians.

Open: *All year except July. Receives men, women, young people, groups and non-retreatants.*
Rooms: *22 singles, 4 doubles.*
Facilities: *Conferences, garden, library, guest lounge and pay phone.*
Spiritual Help: *Personal talks, group sharing, meditation and directed study.*
Guests Admitted to: *Chapel.*
Meals: *Everyone eats together. Traditional food, with provision for vegetarian and special diets.*
Special Activities: *Planned programme of events. Send for brochure.*
Situation: *In the city but quiet.*
Maximum Stay: *By arrangement.*
Bookings: *By letter or telephone.*
Charges: *£24 per day full board per person.*
Access: *London Underground: Docklands Line. Buses: Nos. 5, 15, 40 from Central London.*

St Peter's Community
522 ABC Lordship Lane
Dulwich
London SE26 8LD   Telephone: 081-693 6885

Interdenominational

The Church of England, Roman Catholic monks and lay people of both traditions combined to create an unusual venture at St Peter's. Three Benedictine monks from Worth Abbey shared their life with an

Anglican priest and with laymen who were invited to come as residents for a period as part of their Christian formation. In time others, including women and married people, came to support the venture. Now the monks have returned to Worth Abbey and the wider group that makes up St Peter's continue as an ecumenical lay community. The aim is to maintain the Benedictine spirit with respect to prayer, community and hospitality. This seems a stimulating and exciting challenge and should help St Peter's to continue to provide a good place for retreats.

Open: *All year except August. Receives men, women, groups, and non-retreatants for conferences .*
Rooms: *3 singles, 2 doubles.*
Facilities: *Conferences, garden, library, guest lounge.*
Spiritual Help: *Personal talks .*
Guests Admitted to: *Chapel and work of the community.*
Meals: *Everyone eats together, vegetarians catered for.*
Special Activities: *Programme throughout the year. Send for brochure.*
Situation: *In the city, with a quiet garden, large wood and playing fields behind.*
Maximum Stay: *3 days.*
Bookings: *By letter or telephone.*
Charges: *£16 B&B, £4.50 per person for day with lunch.*
Access: *BR: Forest Hill. Bus: London buses pass the door. Car: South Circular Road near Horniman Museum.*

St Saviour's Priory
18 Queensbridge Road
Haggerston
London E2 8NS   Telephone: 071-739 9976

Anglican

There are no conducted retreats and no group facilities, but a great many people find this a good place for a private retreat.

Open: *Most of the year. Receives women.*
Rooms: *6 singles, 2 doubles.*
Facilities: *Chapel, garden, lounge, TV, pay phone.*
Spiritual Help: *No conducted retreats available but participation in Divine Office.*
Guests Admitted to: *Chapel, garden.*

Meals: *Traditional; DIY available.*
Special Activities: *None.*
Situation: *A purpose-built house in London. Park nearby but in urban environment.*
Maximum Stay: *By arrangement.*
Bookings: *By letter.*
Charges: *No fixed charge but £10 per night suggested minimum to cover costs.*
Access: *By London bus – enquire when booking accepted.*

**The Swaminarayan Hindu Mission
54-62 Meadow Garth
Neasden, London NW10 8HD**   Telephone 081-965 2651

Hindu

The Swaminarayan Hindu Mission is a branch of the worldwide Bochasanwasi Akshar Purushottam Sanstha of India, which is a prominent and charitable Hindu organisation with a wide spectrum of activities including a medical college. It strives to promote social, moral, cultural and spiritual values among all ages within society and has some 3,000 centres and 300 temples around the world. The London Centre is being expanded to include the first major traditional stone and marble Hindu temple in Europe. Facilities will include a community and social centre, a cultural centre, independent day school, sports and recreation facilities, a library, health clinic, prayer hall, conference hall, and marriage registration hall. There is at present a youth organisation and various social, cultural and spiritual activities for men, women, and families. There are a number of other centres in Britain (see below). Information and brochures are available.

Educational Activities include an independent day school in London and centres across Britain hold Sunday schools for children.
Cultural Activities include international childrens' and youth conferences and ' The Cultural Festival of India' held in London in 1985 and in the United States in 1991. Not all such activities are international and many are local or at the Centre in London.
Social Activities is wide ranging and includes such things as social uplifting activities, relief work during times of natural disasters such as those in India and Ethiopia, anti-addiction campaigns, and medical assistance.
Other Centres are in Ashton-under Lyne, Birmingham, Bolton, Bradford, Cardiff, Colchester, Coventry, Crawley, Derby, Hartlepool,

Hertford, Kettering, Leeds, Leicester, Loughborough, Luton, Manchester, Milton Keynes, Northampton, Nottingham, Oldham, Oxford, Peterborough, Preston, Rugby, Southend on Sea, Southampton, Stourbridge, Stoke-on-Trent, Swindon, Walsall, Wellingborough, Wickford, and Wolverhampton.

Tyburn Convent
8 Hyde Park Place
Bayswater Road
London W2 2LJ   Telephone: 071-723 7262

Roman Catholic

Just opposite Hyde Park, the Convent is right in the heart of London. Amid the busy outside world the sisters preside over the perpetual exposition of the Blessed Sacrament – the chapel is open all day and retreat guests may go there at night. Nearby was Tyburn's place of execution, which operated from 1196 to 1783. Following the dissolution of the monasteries, over a hundred officially recognised martyrs died there for their faith and the Convent's Martyrs' Altar is a replica of the Tyburn tree, erected in honour of the memory of its victims.

Open: *All year. Receives men occasionally; women who wish to make a private retreat; groups for day retreats.*
Rooms: *8 singles. Guests are expected to be in by 8.30 p.m. when the Convent is locked.*
Facilities: *Chapel, small garden, library.*
Spiritual Help: *Retreatants are left to spend their time as they wish. If anyone feels the need, they can arrange to talk with a sister.*
Guests Admitted to: *Chapel – a sister is available 3 times a day or by appointment to give individuals or groups a guided tour of the Martyrs' Crypt.*
Meals: *Everyone eats together in the guest house. Traditional food, with provision for vegetarian and special diets (within reason).*
Special Activities: *The perpetual exposition of the Blessed Sacrament in the chapel which is open to the public all day, the full sung Divine Office, and the Shrine of the Martyrs.*
Situation: *In the city but quiet – Hyde Park is across the road.*
Maximum Stay: *10 days.*
Bookings: *By letter or telephone.*
Charges: *By donation.*
Access: *London Underground to Marble Arch. Central London buses. Parking not easy.*

South and South East

Ascot

Society of the Holy Trinity
Ascot Priory
Ascot
Berks. SL5 8RT   Telephone: 0344 882067

Anglican

Open: *All year. Receives men, women, young people, groups and non-retreatants.*
Rooms: *8 singles, 2 doubles.*
Facilities: *Garden, park, guest lounge and pay phone.*
Spiritual Help: *Personal talks and meditation.*
Guests Admitted to: *Chapel.*
Meals: *Very plain, with provision for vegetarian and special diets.*
Special Activities: *No special activities.*
Situation: *Very quiet, in the countryside.*
Maximum Stay: *Unlimited.*
Bookings: *By letter.*
Charges: *By arrangement.*
Access: *Rail and bus both possible. Send for detailed instructions.*

Kintbury

St Cassian's Centre
Kintbury
Berks. RG15 OSR   Telephone: 0488 58267

Roman Catholic – Ecumenical

The De La Salle Brothers run this centre for young people, from sixth-formers to university students, as well as young working people – any young person searching for spiritual growth will be welcomed. Thousands come here to participate in the various sessions, so you need to book about a year in advance. Meals are wholefood and the place is surrounded by gardens, fields and woods.

Open: *Most of year, possibly closed in September. Receives young people mainly. There are family weekends.*
Rooms: *5 singles, 31 doubles.*
Facilities: *Conferences, garden, guest lounges and pay phone.*
Spiritual Help: *Personal talks, group sharing and meditation.*

Guests Admitted to: *Unrestricted access everywhere.*
Meals: *Everyone eats together. Wholefood, with provision for vegetarian and special diets.*
Special Activities: *There is a planned programme of events.*
Situation: *Very quiet, in the countryside.*
Maximum Stay: *Unrestricted.*
Bookings: *By letter.*
Charges: *£40 per head. Monday/Thursday or Thursday/Sunday.*
Access: *BR: Kintbury. Car: via A4.*

Newbury

Cold Ash Centre
The Ridge
Cold Ash
Newbury
Berks. RG16 9HU   Telephone: 0635 65353

Roman Catholic – Interdenominational

The planned programme of retreats here is short but good, offering both preached and directed retreats, Christian meditation and a Franciscan retreat. There are pleasant rooms and fine views. A very popular place so you may need to book up to a year in advance.

Open: *All year except August. Receives men, women, groups and non-retreatants.*
Rooms: *30 singles, 23 doubles.*
Facilities: *Limited disabled (including handrails and a lift), conferences, chapel, library, guest lounge, direct-dialling telephone.*
Spiritual Help: *Personal talks, group sharing, meditation and directed study. Retreats organised for individuals. Groups book for their own needs.*
Guests Admitted to: *Chapel*
Meals: *Taken in the guesthouse. Traditional food with provision for vegetarian.*
Special Activities: *Planned programme of events. Send for leaflet.*
Situation: *Quiet, in the countryside.*
Maximum Stay: *By arrangement.*
Bookings: *By telephone or letter. Deposit required.*
Charges: *Send for details.*
Access: *BR: Thatcham. Bus: Newbury or Reading. Car: Centre is 4 miles from Newbury.*

Newbury

Elmore Abbey
Church Lane
Speen
Newbury
Berks. RG13 1SA   Telephone: 0635 33080

Anglican

Open: *All year except over Christmas. Receives men, non-resident women and non-retreatants.*
Rooms: *5 singles, 4-bed dormitory.*
Facilities: *Garden, library, car park.*
Spiritual Help: *Personal talks, meditation, spiritual counsel, personal assistance with retreat if requested.*
Guests Admitted to: *Chapel and occasionally work of the community.*
Meals: *Everyone eats together. Traditional food, with provision for vegetarians.*
Special Activities: *No planned programme of events.*
Situation: *Very quiet in the village and countryside. Next to the parish church where the community go for the Eucharist on Sundays and major feast days. Guests usually join the community and parishioners.*
Maximum Stay: *1 week.*
Bookings: *By letter.*
Charges: *On application.*
Access: *By rail to Newbury or by car.*

Reading

Douai Abbey
Upper Woolhampton
Reading
Berks. RG7 5TH   Telephone: 0734 713163

Roman Catholic

One of the most famous monastery names – a place for men to make a private retreat in an atmosphere of community prayer. There is a retreat house for both men and women, but here you must cater for yourself. A traditional monastic place in the countryside and yet not far from London, Reading or Oxford.

Open: *All year except Christmas and religious men only in July. Receives men, women, young people, and groups.*
Rooms: *10 singles , 6 doubles.*
Facilities: *Conferences, chapel, garden, guest lounge and telephone.*
Spiritual Help: *Personal talks and sharing in the daily round of prayer.*
Guests Admitted to: *Chapel, choir.*
Meals: *Male guests eat together. Traditional food. Self-catering otherwise.*
Special Activities: *Various events. Send for brochure.*
Situation: *Quiet and in the countryside.*
Maximum Stay: *By arrangement.*
Bookings: *By letter or telephone.*
Charges: *Flexible so enquire but youth accommodation is £7 to £5 per night.*
Access: *BR: Midgham $1^1/_2$ miles. Bus: No. 102 . Car: via M4, Exit 1.*

Windsor

Convent of St John Baptist
Hatch Lane
Windsor
Berks. SL4 3QR   Telephone: 0753 850618

Anglican

The atmosphere is warm and homely here, and you may join the sisters in the convent chapel. They will provide individually directed retreats and personal talks. In addition there is a pleasant garden in which to walk.

Open: *All year, except August. Receives men, women, young people, groups and non-retreatants.*
Rooms: *21 singles.*
Facilities: *Conferences, garden, library, park, guest lounge, TV and pay phone.*
Spiritual Help: *Personal talks, group sharing, meditation, individually directed retreats, one-to-one help. Leaders available for quiet days and retreats.*
Guests Admitted to: *Chapel.*
Meals: *Taken in retreatants' dining room. Traditional and wholefood home-cooking, with provision for vegetarian and special diets. DIY for tea and coffee.*

Special Activities: *'Drop-in Day', planned programme of events. Send for brochure.*
Situation: *Quiet, on the edge of the town. Large garden, separate chapel for retreat use.*
Maximum Stay: *8 days.*
Bookings: *By letter or telephone.*
Charges: *£19 per person per 24 hours.*
Access: *BR: Windsor. Buses: Windsor. Car: via M4, Exit 6.*

HAMPSHIRE

Alton

The Abbey of Our Lady and St John
Alton
Hants. GU34 4AP   Telephone: 0420 62145

Anglican

The Abbey is a setting where you may find stillness and, hopefully, that reflection which may lead to worship and prayer with the community in the Divine Office and daily Mass.

Open: *All year except for Christmas week. Receives men and women. 30 people can be accommodated for a day visit.*
Rooms: *30 singles and 3 twin-bedded rooms.*
Facilities: *Day conferences, garden, guest lounge and pay phone. Children*
Spiritual Help: *Personal talks, conducted retreats, and spiritual direction.*
Guests Admitted to: *Chapel, refectory, and monastery grounds.*
Meals: *Everyone eats together in refectory. Traditional food, with provision for vegetarians. DIY facilities for tea and coffee.*
Special Activities: *A programme of organised events is available. Send for brochure with SAE.*
Situation: *In the countryside. The Abbey provides an opportunity for freedom from everyday pressures in a setting where quiet and reflection lead to worship and prayer at both the daily community Mass and at the Divine Office, celebrated in the monastery church.*
Maximum Stay: *1 week.*
Bookings: *By letter or telephone.*
Charges: *On application. Special consideration is given for*

students, youth groups, and the unemployed.
Access: *BR: Alton, then No. 208 bus. Car: Abbey is off A339.*

Basingstoke

Malshanger Estate
Newfound
Basingstoke
Hants.   Telephone: 071-223 6188
                                                (for enquiries)

Anglican – Ecumenical

Do not call or write to the estate, as it is used by several church groups in London (such as Holy Trinity, Brompton, and All Souls, Langham Place) for group events and for 'Land-Mark Retreats', and you must apply through them (see address below).

Malshanger itself is a large country house in a private estate of over 3,000 acres, with wonderful walks and the use of private squash-courts. The retreats are very much of a renewal and inspirational nature, looking to transformation by the Holy Spirit. A lot of younger adults attend them.

Open: *For retreatants – men, women, young people.*
Rooms: *Singles and doubles are available.*
Facilities: *Bring Bible, notebook, sheets, towel and soap.*
Spiritual Help: *Group sharing, talks.*
Guests Admitted to: *Most facilities.*
Meals: *Depends on event.*
Special Activities: *Planned programme of events. Send for brochure.*
Situation: *Quiet, in the countryside.*
Maximum Stay: *For duration of event only.*
Bookings: *Please contact St Mark's Church, Battersea Rise, London SW11 1EJ in the first instance.*
Charges: *See programme.*
Access: *BR: Basingstoke. Car: via A34, then B3400.*

Most of the trouble in the world is caused by people wanting to be important' – T.S.Eliot

Fareham

Park Place Pastoral Centre
Wickham
Fareham
Hants. PO17 5HA   Telephone: 0329 833043

Roman Catholic

There is lots of room here, including a youth wing with self-catering. All of it is situated in some 18 acres of grounds, overlooking open countryside. The Centre is fairly heavily booked by parish groups, but it is a good place for a family to go on retreat.

Open: *All year except August. Receives men, women, young people, families, groups, religious for spiritual retreats, non-retreatants.*
Rooms: *30 singles, 13 doubles, dormitory.*
Facilities: *Park, guest lounge, library, TV and pay phone.*
Spiritual Help: *Personal talks, group sharing, meditation.*
Guests Admitted to: *Chapel, oratory.*
Meals: *Everyone eats together. Traditional food, with provision for vegetarian. Indian cuisine is served from time to time.*
Special Activities: *Planned programme of events, including guided retreats in meditation in the oriental tradition by Indian Franciscan sisters. Send for brochure.*
Situation: *Very quiet, in the village and countryside.*
Maximum Stay: *5 days.*
Bookings: *By letter.*
Charges: *£25 per person per day.*
Access: *BR: Fareham. Buses: from Southampton, Winchester, then Fareham No. 69. Car: via M3 and A333.*

Farnborough

St Michael's Abbey
Farnborough
Hants. GU14 7NQ   Telephone: 0252 546105

Roman Catholic

The Abbey, built by the Empress Eugenie in 1887, houses the tombs of herself, her husband, Emperor Napoleon III, and her son. In addition to receiving guests and local parish work, the monks operate a bookbindery and a press.

Open: *All year except 23 December to 7 January and during annual community retreat. Receives men, women, young people, groups of up to 12 people, and non-retreatants.*
Rooms: *9 singles, 1 double. 2 singles for men in monastery.*
Facilities: *Disabled day group facilities available, small conferences, garden, park, guest lounge and pay phone.*
Spiritual Help: *Personal talks, group sharing.*
Guests Admitted to: *Chapel, outdoor work of the community if wished.*
Meals: *Traditional food taken in the guest house and in monastery for male guests.*
Special Activities: *None.*
Situation: *In town.*
Maximum Stay: *By arrangement.*
Bookings: *By letter.*
Charges: *By arrangement with guestmaster.*
Access: *BR: Five minutes' walk from Farnborough station. London Link Bus. Car: A325 Camberley to Farnborough.*

Old Alresford

Old Alresford Place
Winchester Diocesan Retreat & Conference Centre
Old Alresford
Hants. SO24 9DH   Telephone: 0962 732518

Anglican

A Georgian 'pile' set in extensive grounds in Old Alresford – the birthplace of the Mothers' Union. Run as a diocesan retreat, conference and training centre, the whole place is tastefully decorated and furnished, the library and meeting rooms light and airy. The team who run the house provide good food and are happy to help with any queries. All the bedrooms are warm and each has a wash basin. One room has been set up for use by a disabled person.

Open: *Most of the year. Receives men, women, young people, families, groups, non-retreatants.*
Rooms: *25 singles, 8 doubles, 3 dormitories.*
Facilities: *Some provision for the disabled, conferences, camping,*

garden, library, guest lounge and pay phone. Children welcomed.
Spiritual Help: *Personal talks, meditation, group sharing, spiritual direction, and counselling.*
Guests Admitted to: *Unrestricted access to all areas, including chapel.*
Meals: *Everyone eats together. Traditional food with provision for vegetarian and special diets.*
Special Activities: *Planned programme of events – send for brochure. Clergy in-service training and lay training courses available.*
Situation: *Very quiet, in the village and countryside.*
Maximum Stay: *Subject to availability.*
Bookings: *By telephone or letter.*
Charges: *£25 per person per day.*
Access: *BR: Alton or Winchester. Bus: from Alton. Car: via A31, then B3046.*

Portsmouth

Catherington House
182 Five Heads Road
Catherington, Waterlooville
Portsmouth
Hants. PO8 9NJ   Telephone: 0705 593251

Anglican

This old red-brick house has provided the stage for half a century of retreat work and caters mainly for parish and diocesan groups, but individuals can be accommodated from time to time when space allows. The house is set in three acres of grounds, with a lovely garden. Healing conferences and weekend holidays are on offer.

Open: *All year except August, Christmas, Easter. Receives men, women, families with children, groups, and non-retreatants.*
Rooms: *7 singles, 10 doubles.*
Facilities: *Conferences, garden, library, guest lounge and pay phone. Children welcome depending on group.*
Guests Admitted to: *Unrestricted access everywhere.*
Meals: *Everyone eats together. Food is 'English', home-cooked with provision for vegetarian and special diets.*
Special Activities: *Planned programme of events. Send for the brochure.*
Situation: *In the village, fairly quiet.*

Maximum Stay: *6 days.*
Bookings: *By telephone or letter.*
Charges: *See brochure.*
Access: *BR: Havant. Bus: from Portsmouth. Car: House is off A3.*

KENT

Maidstone

The Friars
Aylesford
Maidstone
Kent ME20 7BX   Telephone: 0622 717272

Roman Catholic – Ecumenical

The Carmelite Friars say that hope is a source of joy and that joy is a source of strength. At Aylesford they offer an open door to everyone seeking spiritual renewal. The Marian Shrine is a special feature.

Open: *All year except Christmas. Receives men, women, young people, families, groups, religious and non-retreatants.*
Rooms: *26 singles, 33 doubles.*
Facilities: *Conferences, garden, library, guest lounge, tea room, pottery, bookshop. Children welcome.*
Spiritual Help: *Personal talks by prior arrangement. Preached retreats.*
Guests Admitted to: *Chapel, choir.*
Meals: *Guests eat together. Traditional food, with provision for vegetarian and special diets.*
Special Activities: *See brochure for programme. Pilgrimages May to October at Aylesford Priory Shrine.*
Situation: *Mostly quiet, set in the village.*
Maximum Stay: *2 -3 weeks.*
Bookings: *Letter preferred but telephone calls accepted.*
Charges: *£25 per day single, £23 per day shared.*
Access: *BR: Aylesford 1 mile away. Bus: No. 155 from Maidstone East.*

'In prayer it is better to have a heart without words than words without a heart' – John Bunyan

Hailstone

The Seekers Trust
Addington Park
Maidstone, Kent ME19 5BL   Telephone: 0732 843589

Christian

Addington Park is a large place set in some 37 acres of woodlands and gardens. Here the Seekers Trust operate a centre for prayer and spiritual healing with prayer chapels and a healing sanctuary.

Open: *All year. Receives men and women.*
Rooms: *Singles and double flats, each with all DIY facilities.*
Facilities: *Lecture hall, gardens. library, healing sanctuary. No smoking and no pets in guest flats. The accommodation is single storey bungalow, so disabled people should enquire as to suitability.*
Spiritual Help: *Prayer and healing ministry.*
Guests Admitted to: *Everywhere but private residential staff areas.*
Meals: *Guests prepare their own food.*
Special Activities: Prayer and healing.
Situation: *Quiet.*
Maximum Stay: *By arrangement - but usually 2 weeks from April to October and 4 weeks in other months.*
Bookings: *By letter.*
Charges: *Single flat £60 per week, double flat £95 per week for 2 persons and £125 per week for 3 people.*
Access: *BR: Victoria Station to Borough Green, taxi to Addington Park*

Ramsgate

St Augustine's Abbey
Ramsgate
Kent CT11 9PA   Telephone: 0843 593045

Roman Catholic

The guest house was once the home of Pugin and he built the Abbey church. Men are welcomed into the monastic ambience and to share the life of quiet and prayer here – but the community does do parochial work and run a school, which is not on site. You will be expected at Mass and for the Evening Office and Compline.

Open: *All year except Christmas. Receives men and young people.*
Rooms: *6 singles.*
Facilities: *Garden and library.*
Spiritual Help: *Personal talks, meditation.*
Guests Admitted to: *Chapel, with restricted access to some parts of Abbey.*
Meals: *Everyone eats together. Food is traditional.*
Special Activities: *Prayer and quiet is what is offered here.*
Situation: *Rather busy.*
Maximum Stay: *2 weeks.*
Bookings: *By letter.*
Charges: *£10 per day.*
Access: *BR: Ramsgate. Bus: from Ramsgate. Car: via A253.*

Sevenoaks

Stacklands Retreat House
West Kingsdown
Sevenoaks
Kent TN15 6AN   Telephone: 0474 852247

Anglican

The first purpose-built retreat house in England, Stacklands is concerned now with training retreat conductors, but there is a programme of retreats, and individually directed ones are available. It is a quiet place with many acres of grounds in which to wander in order to enhance the atmosphere of solitude and silence.

Open: *All year except Holy Week and Christmas. Receives men, women, young people and groups.*
Rooms: *20 singles.*
Facilities: *Some disabled, garden, library, guest lounge, direct-dialling telephone.*
Spiritual Help: *Personal talks, meditation, directed study, preached addresses and individual interviews.*
Guests Admitted to: *Unrestricted access.*
Meals: *Everyone eats together. Traditional food, with provision for vegetarian and special diets. Optional self-catering for day visitors only.*
Special Activities: *Planned programme of events, training of retreat conductors according to Ignatian methods. Brochure available.*
Situation: *Quiet and in the countryside.*

Maximum Stay: *As arranged.*
Bookings: *By letter or telephone.*
Charges: *Moderate – upon application.*
Access: *BR: from Victoria to Swanley. Bus: not available. Car: via A20.*

Westgate on Sea

St Gabriel's Retreat & Conference Centre
Elm Grove
Westgate on Sea
Kent CT8 8LB   Telephone: 0843 832033

Anglican

Open: *All year except Christmas, Easter and end of August. Receives men, women, young people, groups, families and non-retreatants.*
Rooms: *12 singles, 7 doubles, 2 three-bedded rooms.*
Facilities: *Conferences, garden, library, guest lounge, TV and pay phone. Children welcome.*
Spiritual Help: *Though the Centre mostly attracts self-organised groups, private retreats are available by arrangement, as are quiet days.*
Guests Admitted to: *Chapel.*
Meals: *Everyone eats together. Wholefood, with provision for vegetarian and special diets.*
Special Activities: *Planned programme of events. Send for brochure.*
Situation: *Quiet, at the seaside.*
Maximum Stay: *By arrangement.*
Bookings: *Contact the Warden by letter or telephone.*
Charges: *Send for details.*
Access: *BR: Westgate on Sea. Car: via A28. Ask for detailed directions.*

West Wickham

Emmaus Retreat and Conference Centre
Layhams Road
West Wickham
Kent BR4 9HH   Telephone: 081-777 2000

Roman Catholic – Interfaith

Run by a religious community and a lay team, this rather large centre manages to be very homely and offers good-sized, well-equipped rooms. There are two chapels – one grand and one more modest. Good walks can be taken in the nearby woods. There is a small flat for silent private retreats. The Centre is a popular place for organisations to hold annual retreats and meetings. Yoga meditation weekends are included in the programme.

Open: *All year except over Christmas period. Receives men, women, families, groups, religious and non-retreatants.*
Rooms: *11 singles, 29 doubles, 3 flats.*
Facilities: *Disabled, conferences, 2 chapels, garden, 2 libraries, guest lounge, bookstall, shop, small flat, TV and pay phone. Children welcome.*
Spiritual Help: *Spiritual direction, individually directed retreats, days of prayer and quiet. Personal talks, meditation and group sharing.*
Guests Admitted to: *Chapel and all retreat-house facilities.*
Meals: *Everyone eats together. Traditional meals with provision for vegetarian and special diets.*
Special Activities: *Planned programme of events. Send for brochure.*
Situation: *Quiet, on the edge of the countryside – good walks.*
Maximum Stay: *According to need.*
Bookings: *By telephone or letter.*
Charges: *Send for sheet indicating proposed offerings.*
Access: *BR: Hayes, Bromley South or East Croydon. Bus: No. 119. Car: Centre is near A232.*

MIDDLESEX

Harrow on the Hill

St Mary's Vicarage Annexe
Church Hill
Harrow on the Hill
Middlesex HA1 3HL   Telephone: 081-422 2652

Anglican

The annexe at St Mary's Vicarage is a self-contained wing which has been converted to accommodate small groups and individual retreatants comfortably. It is self-catering. Not a suitable site or place

for the disabled. Most groups bring a leader but personal consultation
is available as required.

Open: *All year. Receives men, women, young people, families,
groups, and non-retreatants.*
Rooms: *5 singles, 1 double, 10 bunk bed accommodation.*
Facilities: *Small conferences, garden, library, TV and pay phone.
Children welcomed.*
Spiritual Help: *Personal talks if required. This is a good place
for individuals or small groups to use for study, discussion and
prayer.*
Guests Admitted to: *Unrestricted access to all areas and to church
next door.*
Meals: *Self-catering.*
Special Activities: *Send for brochure.*
Situation: *In an area of character amidst the vast suburban sprawl
of West London. Next door is the 900-year-old Church of St Mary,
while beyond the churchyard stretch woods and open fields.*
Maximum Stay: *2 weeks.*
Bookings: *By letter or telephone.*
Charges: *£30 overnight stay, £20 per day, £15 half day.*
Access: *By London Underground, bus or car.*

Pinner

The Grail
Waxwell Farm House
125 Waxwell Lane
Pinner
Middlesex HA5 3ER   Telephone: 081-866 2195/0505

Roman Catholic – Ecumenical

Just 25 minutes from Baker Street Underground station, the centre
stands in some 10 acres of grounds. It offers small cedar-wood chalets
set in the woods, where you can experience 'poustinia', which in
Russian means 'a place apart'. Here you may live in silence, reflection
and prayer like a hermit. Some food is supplied for you to prepare
yourself, while some meals are brought to you ready-made. There is
an extensive programme of events and courses, one of which is a
family week, which provides a good opportunity for adults to be
together and the children to be cared for – not exactly a retreat but at
least a good start in that direction. The centre is run by a Catholic lay

community of women, and everyone of whatever faith, or of none, is welcomed.

Open: *Most of the year. Receives men, women, young people, families, groups and non-retreatants.*

Rooms: *3 singles, 14 doubles, 1 dormitory, hermitage chalets - one for winter, six for summer.*

Facilities: *Conferences, large garden, library, guest lounge and pay phone. Children welcome during family week. Pets allowed.*

Spiritual Help: *Personal talks, Charismatic group each week, assistance with meditation if in hermitage only.*

Guests Admitted to: *Chapel and work of the community.*

Meals: *Everyone eats together. Traditional food, with provision for vegetarian and special diets. DIY in hermitages..*

Special Activities: *Planned programme of events. Send for brochure.*

Situation: *Quiet, on edge of London.*

Maximum Stay: *Receives individual guests between group events, so enquire.*

Bookings: *By letter or telephone.*

Charges: *Send for details as there are various charges.*

Access: London Underground, Baker Street to Pinner. Bus: from Harrow.

SURREY

Godalming

Ladywell Retreat Centre
Ladywell Convent
Ashstead Lane
Godalming
Surrey GU7 1ST   Telephone: 0483 423 764
Roman Catholic

Near to Ladywell is an ancient shrine on one of the main old pilgrim routes to Canterbury. Guests who only want a holiday or to rest, and are not prepared to make an effort to use the contemplative environment to seek peace through prayer, should try another place. Individually directed retreats and on-going spiritual direction are available to help each person along this path, combined with the community's notable spirit of hospitality. The retreat centre itself is in a wing of the main building with a small oratory and prayer room.

Open: *All year. Receives men, women, young people, and groups.*
Rooms: *27 singles and 2 doubles. Accommodation for day groups of up to 100.*
Facilities: *Disabled – with lifts to bedrooms and a loop system for the hard of hearing – garden, library, guest lounge and pay phone.*
Spiritual Help: *Directed retreats.*
Guests Admitted to: *Chapel, choir and work of the community.*
Meals: *Guests eat together. Freshly cooked traditional food, with provision for vegetarian and special diets.*
Special Activities: *Planned programme of events. Send for brochure.*
Situation: *Quiet, in the countryside, with spacious grounds and gardens.*
Maximum Stay: *8 day retreat.*
Bookings: *By telephone, but confirm by letter.*
Charges: *£22 per person per day (residential).*
Access: *By rail or car.*

Hindhead

Cenacle Retreat House
Headley Road
Grayshott
Hindhead
Surrey GU 26 6DN   Telephone: 0428 604412

Roman Catholic

Cenacle means 'upper chamber' and refers to the room where the Last Supper was held. The sisters belong to an international congregation ministering to men and women of all faiths. There is an extensive retreat programme, including courses and both directed and private retreats aimed at human and faith development.

Open: *Nearly all year. Receives men, women, young people, families and groups.*
Rooms: *21 singles, 9 doubles.*
Facilities: *Large garden, library, and pay phone.*
Spiritual Help: *Adult faith education, spiritual direction and a range of retreats and workshops aimed at personal and spiritual development. Personal talks, groups sharing, meditation.*
Guests admitted to: *Chapel, prayer room.*
Meals: *Everyone eats together Traditional food with provision for vegetarians and DIY for tea and coffee. Medical special diets only*

are catered for.
Special Activities: *Planned programme. Send for brochure.*
Situation: *Very quiet, less than a mile from the village. Within easy walking distance are some beautiful National Trust properties.*
Maximum Stay: *By negotiation but 30-day retreat stays are possible.*
Bookings: *By letter or telephone.*
Charges: *£28 per 24 hrs for accommodation. See brochure for other charges.*
Access: *BR: from Waterloo to Haslemere. Bus: No.268 from Hindhead and Haslemere will stop on request. Car: via A3 to B3002.*

Richmond

**St Michael's Convent
56 Ham Common
Richmond
Surrey TW10 7JH**   Telephone: 081-940 8711

Anglican

St Michael's Convent is a smart place on Ham Common in Richmond, with the park nearby for walks and a large garden in which to sit. The community has a special interest in the idea of prayer and the clown, running 'clown' workshops as part of its activity programme, which also includes sessions on prayer and painting and a 10-day retreat, usually in August, for women 18–30 to live with the community and experience a life of prayer and fellowship.

Open: *Almost all year. Receives men, women, and groups.*
Rooms: *6 singles, 3 doubles. Bring your own towel.*
Facilities: *Disabled – loop system for the deaf in chapel and conference areas, lift by request. Garden, park, library, guest lounge, telephone.*
Spiritual Help: *Personal talks, group sharing, meditation, spiritual direction, guided retreats and workshops such as "painting and the inner journey". Eucharist most days.*
Guests Admitted to: *Chapel. Help often welcomed in the garden.*
Meals: *Everyone eats silently together. Traditional food with provision for vegetarian and special diets.*
Special Activities: *Planned programme of events. Send for brochure.*
Situation: *Quiet, but only 8 miles from Heathrow. Situated in a suburban area near Richmond Park, with access to the Thames.*

Maximum Stay: *By arrangement.*
Bookings: *By letter with s.a.e., please.*
Charges: *£15 per day.*
Access: *By rail, bus or car.*

Woking

St. Columba's House
Maybury Hill
Woking
Surrey GU22 8AB   Telephone: 0483 766498

Anglican

St. Columba's welcomes men and women of all faiths or none and provides a common ground for ecumenical discussion and prayer. There are Myers-Briggs weekends, prayer and music retreats and 8-day guided retreats in the programme of activities.

Open: *All year, except August and Christmas. Receives men, women, young people, groups and non-retreatants. Women religious for holidays and convalescence in convent.*
Rooms: *25 singles.*
Facilities: *Disabled, conferences, garden, library, guest lounge, TV and pay phone.*
Spiritual Help: *Personal talks, meditation, individually guided retreats.*
Guests Admitted to: *Unrestricted within retreat area, chapel.*
Meals: *Everyone eats together. Traditional food with provision for vegetarian and special diets.*
Special Activities: *Planned programme of events. Send for brochure.*
Situation: *Very quiet, in the countryside. Retreat house is within the grounds of the convent.*
Maximum Stay: *1 week.*
Bookings: *By letter or telephone.*
Charges: *£20 per day, full board.*
Access: *BR: from Waterloo station to Woking (1 mile from house). Car: via Maybury Hill off the B382 – avoid entering Woking town. Good map available in brochure*

Forest Row

Emerson College
Forest Row
East Sussex RH18 5JX   Telephone: 034 282 2238

New Age – Interdenominational

The College is named after the American philosopher Ralph Waldo Emerson, who believed in building a harmonious relationship between nature and the human imagination. The educationalist Rudolph Steiner translated this into practical methods for achieving spiritual development, and Emerson College is one of several establishments which recognise Emerson's work. It is open to all men and women who have the will 'to serve truly human needs and the needs of the earth at this crucial time in history'.

Open: *From Christmas to Epiphany. During the remainder of the year the College offers courses and conferences. Receives men, women and young people.*
Rooms: *8 singles.*
Facilities: *Garden, park, library, guest lounge and telephone. No DIY facilities or TV. Children and pets not permitted.*
Spiritual Help: *Lectures, workshops and study groups.*
Guests Admitted to: *Unrestricted access.*
Meals: *Everyone eats together. Wholefood, with provision for vegetarian and special diets.*
Special Activities: *Planned programme of events. Send for brochure.*
Situation: *Very quiet and in the countryside.*
Maximum Stay: *12–14 days.*
Bookings: *By letter or telephone.*
Charges: *See programme.*
Access: *BR to East Grinstead and then by taxi. Enquire in letter as to best car route.*

Heathfield

Monastery of the Visitation
Waldron
nr. Heathfield
East Sussex TN21 ORX   Telephone: 04353 2619

Roman Catholic

The sisters are called to be a praying presence in the world and they offer an environment of stillness, prayer and spiritual renewal to those women who wish to share their lives for a time. This is a place for silence.

Open: *Easter to November. Receives women and girls over 16.*
Rooms: *3 singles.*
Facilities: *Garden, park, library and direct-dialling telephone.*
Spiritual Help: *Personal talks, daily sharing in the Divine Office. Resident chaplain available if necessary.*
Guests Admitted to: *Unrestricted access within the enclosure, in addition to chapel, choir and work with community in the garden and kitchen garden.*
Meals: *Everyone eats together. Plain food, with provision for vegetarian and special diets. Self-catering for hot drinks.*
Special Activities: *No planned programme outside the daily structure and space for prayer.*
Situation: *Very quiet – set in the countryside in 50 acres of parkland, with beautiful views over South Downs.*
Maximum Stay: *1 week.*
Bookings: *By letter or telephone.*
Charges: *Terms available on application.*
Access: *By rail and bus to Uckfield, then by taxi to the Monastery.*

Hove

The Monastery of Christ the Saviour
23 Cambridge Road
Hove
East Sussex BN3 1DE   Telephone: 0273 726698

Anglican

Founded in 1985 in a run-down area of Hove, these members of the Community of the Servants of the Will of God live a corporate life of silence, work, and prayer, providing a foundation for the renewal of the local church. Daily worship is held in the parish church and the monks are engaged as well in teaching and spiritual direction. The large 19th century house was formerly used as flats. These have been renovated as a monastery to include guest accommodation.

Open: *All year. Receives men and women.*
Rooms: *2 singles.*

Facilities: *Library. No radios or transistors are allowed.*
Spiritual Help: *Personal talks.*
Guests Admitted to: *Chapel.*
Meals: *Everyone eats together. Traditional food.*
Special Activities: *None, but information sheet about the community and its daily life is available.*
Situation: *Reasonably quiet. In a town.*
Maximum Stay: *By arrangement.*
Bookings: *By letter or telephone.*
Charges: *Donation of up to £10 per day.*
Access: *By rail or bus to Brighton/Hove.*

SUSSEX (WEST)

Arundel

Convent of Poor Clares
Crossbush
Arundel
West Sussex BN18 9PJ   Telephone: 0903 88 2536
                                             0903 88 3125

Roman Catholic

Open: *All year except 1 November to 8 December and over Christmas. Receives women and men (with references.)*
Rooms: *4 singles, 1 double.*
Facilities: *Caravans, small library, guest lounge, TV and guest telephone.*
Spiritual Help: *Personal talks.*
Guests Admitted to: *Chapel.*
Meals: *House guests only. Traditional food, with provision for vegetarians and special diets. Caravan guests use DIY facilities for meals.*
Special Activities: *Guests mostly enjoy a quiet time or a private retreat, and join the sisters at prayer.*
Situation: *House is quiet but on a very busy road. Lovely countryside with good walks nearby. Few miles from the coast.*
Maximum Stay: *2 weeks.*
Bookings: *By letter.*
Charges: *No set charge but £15 a night per person covers costs.*
Access: *BR: Arundel station 5 minutes away. No easy buses. Car: via A27.*

Bognor Regis

St Joseph's
Albert Road
Bognor Regis
West Sussex PO21 1NJ   Telephone: 0243 864051

Roman Catholic

Open: *All year except for Christmas and Easter. Receives men, women, young people, families, groups and non-retreatants.*
Rooms: *Single rooms available, plus 2 doubles and a hermitage.*
Facilities: *Garden, library, guest lounge, TV and pay phone. Children and pets welcomed.*
Spiritual Help: *Chaplain available.*
Guests Admitted to: *Chapel, choir, work of Community.*
Meals: *Everyone eats together – food is traditional. Self-catering available. No provision for vegetarians.*
Special Activities: *No planned programme of events.*
Situation: *Quiet. In the town close to promenade – countryside nearby.*
Maximum Stay: *2 weeks.*
Bookings: *By letter.*
Charges: *By donation.*
Access: *By rail, bus or car.*

Chichester

St Francis House
30 Parchment Street
Chichester
West Sussex PO19 3BX   Telephone: 0243 788345

Interdenominational

All events at St Francis House are ecumenical. It is a private house which Miss Patricia Holmes opens to guests seeking tranquillity in a Christian atmosphere. Prayer workshops, meditation, quiet days and prayer and painting weekends are available. Miss Holmes is an Open Door and an Ignation directed-retreat leader.

Open: *All year. Receives women on individually guided retreats and as non-retreatants.*

Rooms: *2 singles.*
Facilities: *Garden, guest lounge.*
Spiritual Help: *Personal talks, meditation, group sharing, and help in spiritual direction.*
Guests Admitted to: *Prayer/quiet room.*
Meals: *Eaten in the dining-room. Traditional food, with provision for vegetarian and special diets. Self-catering if required.*
Special Activities: *Small, quiet retreat house giving opportunity for a rest, for 'space' or for directed retreat. 3-day retreats.*
Situation: *Quiet, in the city.*
Maximum Stay: *6 days.*
Bookings: *By letter.*
Charges: *£15 per person full board, reduction for half-board and self-catering.*
Access: *By rail or car (route map in brochure).*

Crawley

Grace & Compassion Convent
Paddockhurst Road
Turners Hill
Crawley
West Sussex RH10 4GZ   Telephone: 0342 715672

Roman Catholic

Open: *As available. Receives men, women, young people and non-retreatants.*
Rooms: *1 double (or single).*
Facilities: *Small garden. Children and pets may be admitted by special arrangement.*
Spiritual Help: *Basically a quiet place, with space for reflection.*
Guests Admitted to: *Chapel.*
Meals: *Everyone eats together, or can eat alone if this is preferred. Traditional food, with kettle and toaster for guest use.*
Special Activities: *No structured programme.*
Situation: *In the countryside but rather busy.*
Maximum Stay: *2 weeks.*
Bookings: *By letter or telephone.*
Charges: *By donation.*
Access: *BR to Three Bridges. No bus. Car route from Crawley.*

Crawley

Monastery of the Holy Trinity
Crawley Down
Crawley
West Sussex RH10 4LH   Telephone: 0342 712074

Anglican

This is an enclosed contemplative order for men. Guests are asked to respect the timetable and silence of the monks' daily life. This is not a suitable retreat place for those who are under psychological stress or feel that they could not 'handle' silence and lack of conversation.

Open: *All year. Receives men and women.*
Rooms: *6 singles.*
Facilities: *Library and telephone.*
Spiritual Help: *Participation in the Divine Office and group prayer, including the Jesus prayer.*
Guests Admitted to: *Chapel, grounds of monastery except monastic enclosure, work of the community.*
Meals: *Everyone eats together. Wholefood with provision for vegetarians.*
Special Activities: *None.*
Situation: *Very quiet, in the midst of woodland, with a small farm.*
Maximum Stay: *1 week.*
Bookings: *By letter or telephone.*
Charges: *£10 per day.*
Access: *BR: to Three Bridges. Bus: to Crawley and change for Crawley Down. Car: via M23, Exit 10.*

Crawley

Worth Abbey
Crawley
West Sussex RH10 4SB   Telephone: 0342 715911

Roman Catholic

Education and pastoral work are the business of this community, and there is a school within the grounds, but the setting is beautiful and quiet can be found.

Open: *All year except 24 December to 6 January and August. Receives men only for the time being.*
Rooms: *5 singles.*
Facilities: *Use of library by arrangement with librarian. Guest lounge and pay phone.*
Spiritual Help: *Personal talks.*
Guests Admitted to: *Unrestricted access within the grounds, chapel, choir and educational and pastoral work.*
Meals: *Everyone eats together. Traditional food, with provision for vegetarians. Self-catering kitchenette.*
Special Activities: *Guests are welcome to attend the Monastic Office 4 times daily as well as the Conventual Mass.*
Situation: *In the countryside, with beautiful grounds, but there is a school on the campus.*
Maximum Stay: *Ordinarily 4 nights, 1 week if making a retreat.*
Bookings: *By letter.*
Charges: *No set charge but donations appreciated.*
Access: *BR: from Victoria station to Three Bridges. Car: via M23, Exit 10 to East Grinstead.*

East Grinstead

Neale House Conference Centre
Moat Road
East Grinstead
West Sussex RH19 3LB   Telephone: 0342 312552

Anglican - Interdenominational

Neale House offers a centre from which to explore the Sussex countryside and there are plenty of things to do locally. It is usual for groups who have arranged their own special retreat programme to come to stay, but special help on spiritual matters can be arranged for individuals.

Open: *Weekends lasting from Friday supper to Sunday tea-time. Receives men, women, young people, families, groups, and non-retreatants. Closed August and Christmas.*
Rooms: *5 singles, 8 doubles, 3 dormitories.*
Facilities: *Conferences, garden, park, guest lounge, TV and pay phone. Children welcomed. Pets permitted.*
Spiritual Help: *Guests usually get on with their own programme of activities but can call for help – guidance includes personal*

talks and group sharing.
Guests Admitted to: *Unrestricted access.*
Meals: *Everyone eats together. Traditional food, with provision for vegetarian and special diets if required.*
Special Activities: *Guests usually come in groups, having arranged their own programme.*
Situation: *'Quietish', on edge of town, close to Sussex countryside.*
Maximum Stay: *No limit.*
Bookings: *By letter or telephone.*
Charges: *£50 per person per weekend.*
Access: *By rail to East Grinstead then a 10 minute walk. Car : A22*

Hassocks

Priory of Our Lady
Sayers Common
Hassocks
West Sussex BN6 9HT   Telephone: 0273 832901

Roman Catholic

'One heart and one soul in God' sums up the way of life of this flourishing Augustinian monastic community. All men and women of good faith, whether Christian, Buddhist, Hindu or Jew, are welcomed by the sisters at their delightful modern priory set at the end of a drive that is edged with daffodils in the spring. There is a retreat centre in a separate house for guests and a simpler but good programme ranging from a weekend on awareness of the invisible and the meaning of prayer to an adventure in painting and prayer. **Highly recommended.**

Open: *All year except mid-August to mid-September. Receives men, women, young people, families, groups and occasionally non-retreatants. Taking children is possible but the facilities are not really very suitable.*
Rooms: *3 singles, 14 doubles, dormitory with 4 beds.*
Facilities: *Conferences, garden, library, guest lounge, TV and pay phone. Children welcomed. No pets.*
Spiritual Help: *Personal talks.*
Guests Admitted to: *Chapel, choir and community prayers in the church.*
Meals: *Taken in guest house. Traditional food, vegetarians catered for.*
Special Activities: *Planned programme of events. Send for brochure.*
Situation: *Quiet and in the countryside.*

Maximum Stay: *8 days*
Bookings: *By letter.*
Charges: *Upon application.*
Access: *By bus, which stops at Sayers Common, or by car.*

Haywards Heath

The Convent of the Holy Rood
Lindfield
Haywards Heath
West Sussex RH16 2RA   Telephone: 04447 2345

Christian

After almost a century of nursing the elderly, this community has moved into a new convent. They have adapted space in a guest house they own in Lindfield to offer quiet days for guests and the facilities for those who want to organise conferences and group retreats. This is a small community of elderly religious and, while there are limitations on the facilities, the right atmosphere is created for achieving peace and reflection.

Open: *All year. Receives men, women, young people and clergy.*
Rooms: *Single rooms for two or three guests.*
Facilities: *A hall for small groups is available*
Spiritual Help: *Short-term retreats and quiet days.*
Guests Admitted to: *Unrestricted access within guest areas.*
Meals: *Guests eat together.*
Special Activities: *None*
Situation: *Quiet.*
Maximum Stay: *By arrangement.*
Bookings: *By letter or telephone.*
Charges: *On request.*
Access: *Ask for BR details and bus routes when applying.*

Horsham

Monastery of the Visitation
Partridge Green
Horsham
West Sussex RH13 8EG   Telephone: 0403 710328

Roman Catholic

Here is a straightforward place for the serious retreatant, who will be asked not to leave the enclosure during her period of retreat. The setting is peaceful and not far from London.

Open: *All year round except Holy Week, Easter and 21 December to 1 February. Receives women.*
Rooms: *2 singles.*
Facilities: *Limited, but reading material for study purposes is likely to be available.*
Spiritual Help: *Personal talks, meditation.*
Guests Admitted to: *Chapel, choir and work of the community.*
Meals: *Everyone eats together. Very plain food, with provision for vegetarian and special diets. Self-catering for drinks.*
Special Activities: *No planned programme of events.*
Situation: *Very quiet, in the countryside, a half mile from the village.*
Maximum Stay: *For the agreed period of the retreat.*
Bookings: *Preferably by letter.*
Charges: *£5 per person per day, £30 per person per week.*
Access: *BR: from Victoria station to Horsham. Buses: Nos. 107 or 137 run every hour from Horsham to Partridge Green.*

Horsham

St Julian's Community
Coolham
Horsham
West Sussex RH13 8QL   Telephone: 0403 741220

Ecumenical

Founded almost 50 years ago, St Julian's is a small lay community made up of people who are trying to achieve a happy and fulfilling existence by relating Christ's teaching about love to modern life and thought. The Community and their guests live together in a small manor-house overlooking a lake and surrounded by fields. They do not take new guests over normal retirement age, because as a popular retreat place they have found that younger people do not book very far in advance unlike retired people and, therefore, there are often no rooms left for younger guests. The purpose, also, of the Community's hospitality is for those who need a break from a busy, working life.

Open: *All year except for special periods. Receives men and women.*
Rooms: *9 singles, 7 doubles.*
Facilities: *Chapel, garden with lake surrounded by trees, library, guest lounge, pay phone. No pets.*
Spiritual Help: *The purpose of the house is to provide a peaceful place for people of whatever religion, denomination or occupation - but not age - who want a pause from the pressures of life to read, rest and enjoy the country.*
Guests Admitted to: *Chapel guests are welcome at morning and evening prayers.*
Meals: *Taken in the dining room in silence, no special diets.*
Special Activities: *None.*
Situation: *Set in extensive grounds containing a 5-acre lake with wildfowl and swans.*
Maximum Stay: *By arrangement.*
Bookings: *By telephone or letter.*
Charges: *£26 per person per day.*
Access: *BR: Billingshurst station, then by taxi. Car: from Horsham take A24; after 4–5 miles turn right on to A272, signposted Billingshurst. St Julian's is 2 $1/_2$ miles on the left.*

ISLE OF WIGHT

Ryde

Quarr Abbey
Ryde
Isle of Wight PO33 4ES   Telephone: 0983 882420

Roman Catholic

Here is a place for men to share for a few days in the life of a Benedictine community, following a daily life of worship with time for reading and prayer.

Open: *Most of year. Receives men.*
Rooms: *10 singles in guest house.*
Facilities: *Disabled people by prior arrangement. chapel, library, bookstall, guest lounge.*
Spiritual Help: *Mass and Divine Office held daily in Gregorian chant. Opportunities exist to discuss spiritual matters with one of the Guest Masters.*
Guests Admitted to: *Chapel, refectory, monastery grounds, and to*

share in community work.
Meals: *Everyone eats in refectory. DIY for drinks.*
Special Activities: *No planned programme.*
Situation: *Near sea, farm and countryside, woodlands.*
Maximum Stay: *By arrangement.*
Bookings: *By letter or telephone.*
Charges: *By donation according to means.*
Access: *Ferry to Ryde from Portsmouth.*

Ryde

St Cecilia's Abbey
Ryde
Isle of Wight PO33 1LH   Telephone: 0983 562602

Roman Catholic

Divine Office is sung in Gregorian chant by this Benedictine community of nuns. Many people find great serenity and rest in this peaceful, modal music and in the tranquil rhythm of the liturgy and psalmody. Moreover, the Abbey itself is a very quiet place near the sea.

Open: *All year except Christmas and Holy Week. Receives women and married couples.*
Rooms: *2 singles, 3 doubles.*
Facilities: *Small garden.*
Spiritual Help: *Personal talks. Visitors are free to attend services in their part of the church.*
Guests Admitted to: *Extern chapel of the Abbey church.*
Meals: *Traditional food taken in the guest house.*
Special Activities: *Some years ago, to mark the 15th centenary of St Benedict's birth, a set of slides, with a running commentary on cassette, was made to illustrate the Benedictine monastic life. The slides are still shown occasionally.*
Situation: *Quiet, on the outskirts of a seaside town. Walks in the countryside. Easy access to shopping centre and bus tours of the island.*
Maximum Stay: *1 week provisionally.*
Bookings: *By letter.*
Charges: *No fixed charge - according to each case and by donation.*
Access: *By ferry. Taxi from landing stage if required.*

South West

Bath

The Ammerdown Centre
Radstock
Bath
Avon BA5 5SW   Telephone: 0761 433709

Ecumenical

In principle Ammerdown is more a laity centre than a retreat house but, having said that, they do offer an excellent range of retreat courses and provide people who wish to get away from it all the choice of two 'prayer flats'. Study, personal growth, ecumenical dialogue, and group development are the aims of the courses. The Centre occupies various attractive old buildings in and around the stable-block of Ammerdown House, the private residence of Lord Hylton and his family. Some of the parklands and gardens are open to residents. While predominantly Christian, the governing body represents other religious communities. For example, one of the governors has been the well-known Rabbi Lionel Blue. The activities programme reflects this ecumenical base and has incorporated, for instance, studies on Julian of Norwich, the early English Christian mystic; icons and the spiritual traditions of the Orthodox Church; and Jewish/Christian Liberation Theology. There is plenty on offer both for the first-time private retreatant and for those who attend religious conferences regularly.

Open: *All year except Christmas. Receives men, women, young people, groups.*
Rooms: *32 single, 4 doubles; 2 prayer flats for a maximum of 3 people; peace cottage for young people.*
Facilities: *Disabled (2 ground-floor rooms with a toilet/bathroom), conferences, garden, park, library, guest lounge, licensed bar, TV and phone.*
Spiritual Help: *Personal talks, group sharing and meditation during planned courses, directed study.*
Guests Admitted to: *Unrestricted access, chapel.*
Meals: *Everyone eats together. DIY facilities. Food is traditional, wholesome and plentiful, with provision for vegetarian and special diets.*
Special Activities: *A very good programme. See brochure. There is a special annexe for day groups.*
Situation: *Very quiet, in the countryside.*
Maximum Stay: *By arrangement.*

Bookings: *By letter or telephone.*
Charges: *On application.*
Access: *BR: to Bath Spa. Buses: to Radstock. Car: Centre is just off A362.*

Bath

Bainesbury House
Downside Abbey
Stratton on the Fosse
Bath
Avon BA5 4RH   Telephone: 0761 232845

Christian

The retreat house, owned by Downside Abbey, is open to all Christian groups and is self-catering.

Open: *All year. Receives families and groups - but do enquire if you do not fit into these categories (see other entry for Downside Abbey.)*
Rooms: *Singles and dormitories. Check when booking on exact arrangements.*
Facilities: *Abbey church, garden, park, library, guest lounge, telephone by arrangement. Children welcomed.*
Spiritual Help: *Groups usually look after their own programme. However, members of the monastic community are available to Roman Catholics for sacramental needs, and are prepared, if required, to give talks, lead meditations and give personal spiritual guidance for all visitors.*
Guests Admitted to: *Access to nearby Abbey church.*
Meals: *Self-catering*
Special Activities: *No planned programme. Groups arrange their own.*
Situation: *Quiet, near the village, about 12 miles from Bath.*
Maximum Stay:
Bookings: *By letter.*
Charges:
Access: *BR: to Bath Spa. Bus: from Bath Spa to Stratton on the Fosse. Car: via A367.*

'In the joy of others lies our own, in the progress of others rests our own.' His Divine Holiness Pramukh Swami Maharaj

Bath

Downside Abbey
Stratton on the Fosse
Bath
Avon BA5 4RH   Telephone: 0761 232295

Roman Catholic

The home of a famous boys' public school, with an abbey church of cathedral proportions. The community welcomes men who wish to share the monastic prayer and quiet, or who may want a peaceful base for a holiday. This is very much a hard-working place with a busy schedule, but the Guestmaster is usually available for a personal talk and to help with spiritual guidance.

Open: *All year except Christmas and mid-July to mid-August. Receives men only.*
Rooms: *10 singles.*
Facilities: *Abbey church, garden, library (by permission), guest lounge.*
Spiritual Help: *Monks give guests help and guidance when they have time; the Guestmaster is more readily available for personal talks and directed study.*
Guests Admitted to: *Chapel, otherwise outer enclosure. Guests are asked not to enter the school area.*
Meals: *Everyone eats together. Traditional food.*
Special Activities: *No planned programme.*
Situation: *Quiet, near the village, about 12 miles from Bath.*
Maximum Stay: 1 week.
Bookings: *By letter only, please.*
Charges: *None but donations expected.*
Access: *BR: to Bath Spa. Bus: from Bath Spa to Stratton on the Fosse. Car: via A367.*

Bristol

Emmaus House
Clifton Hill
Clifton
Bristol BS8 4PD   Telephone: 0272 738056

Roman Catholic

On the hills of Clifton looking out across the Cumberland Basin to green hills, the Sisters of La Retraite continue their 300-year-old Congregation tradition of work in retreats and education and human growth programmes. There is no messing about here - the facilities at Emmaus House are 'state of the art', ranging from video cameras for conferences to a Creation Block that provides resources for creative activities such as painting and pottery, or for relaxation, such as a Jacuzzi and a Zen garden. The oratory in which you may pray and meditate is a simple room in which silence itself is the major decoration. Modern facilities, combined with a relaxed atmosphere and good food, all help to enhance the retreatant's physical well-being and spiritual growth. The Myers-Briggs courses are on offer, including a basic workshop, together with courses on stress, spiritual life and prayer, leadership and 'type dynamics'. Other workshops reflect a New Age, holistic approach. Subjects include healing and integration of the feminine and masculine; nurturing and healing the body; spirituality for the Third Age; and a holistic-centred journey over a six-day retreat period. **Highly recommended.**

Open: *All year except Christmas. Receives men, women, groups, and non-retreatants.*
Rooms: *15 Singles, 2 doubles.*
Facilities: *Loop-system for deaf in hall, conference facilities including TV, video camera and most necessary equipment, garden, bookshop, Liturgy resource centre, TV, pay phone. No smoking.*
Spiritual Help: *Personal talks, group sharing, meditation, direction for retreats, counselling, spiritual direction. 30-day retreats and individual retreats.*
Guests Admitted to: *Chapel.*
Meals: *Everyone eats together. Wholefood, with provision for vegetarians but not for special diets.*
Special Activities: *Full programme of adult education, personal and spiritual growth courses and retreats. Send for brochure.*
Situation: *In town. Amount of noise depends on group in house at any given time. Lovely views and pleasant neighbourhood.*
Maximum Stay: *8-day retreat.*
Bookings: *By telephone, but must confirm by letter.*
Charges: *Available on request as charges vary depending on what you are doing and the length of stay.*
Access: *BR: to Bristol Temple Meads. Bus: No. 8 from station to W. H. Smith in Clifton Down Road. Car: from north take M5, Exit 17, then A4018; from London take M4, Exit 20, then M5, Exit 19, followed by A369.*

Bristol

Omega Order
'The Priory' Winford Manor
Winford
Bristol BS18 8DW   Telephone: 0275 872262

Ecumenical

The Order was founded in 1980, taking its title from the words of
Christ – 'I am the Alpha and the Omega, the first and the last.' The
Priory has gone from strength to strength over the last few years and
guests are welcomed at all times, either to attend courses and retreats,
or to find space for rest and reflection and to join the community of
lay and religious men and women in the rhythm of a life of prayer.
Courses include retreats to enhance insight, through the study of
calligraphy, contemplative dance, Christian and Buddhist spirituality, new and scientific concepts of God, and creativity is encouraged
through drawing, poetry and working with wax. There are also
traditional courses on contemplative prayer and meditation. The
Prior, Canon Peter Spink, has written a number of books, and the
Order has produced a series of cassettes and offers a correspondence
course to help participants develop their own perceptions and insights.
In short, Winford Manor offers silence in which to reflect and studies
in which to expand and develop consciousness of the spirit. A good
location for those who may not want their first retreat to be in a church
setting that is overwhelmingly traditional. Indeed here is a place
where you will be taken seriously if you ask why God is referred to
as masculine – and you will get a considered answer.

Open: *All year. Receives men, women, young people, families,
groups, and those who simply want to rest.*
Rooms: *15 singles, 5 doubles, cottage.*
Facilities: *Disabled, garden, park, library, guest lounge, and pay
phone. Children welcomed, pets permitted.*
Spiritual Help: *Personal talks, group sharing, meditation, directed
study.*
Guests Admitted to: *Chapel and work of the community.*
Meals: *Everyone eats together. International food with provision for
vegetarian and special diets.*
Special Activities: *Planned programme of events, including dance,
meditation, and calligraphy. Send for brochure.*
Situation: *Quiet, near village and countryside. Old manor-house
standing in 7 acres of wooded grounds.*

Maximum Stay: *Unlimited.*
Bookings: *By letter.*
Charges: *£20 upwards per person per 24 hours, so see tariff.*
Access: *BR: Bristol Temple Meads station 7 miles away.*
Buses: Central Bristol Bus Station. Car: via A38 from Bristol to Exeter Road.

CORNWALL

Helston

Trelowarren Fellowship
Mawgan in Meneage
Helston
Cornwall TR12 6AD   Telephone: 032622 366

Christian – Interdenominational

Located in an ancient manor-house buried in the heart of the countryside, the Fellowship is open to Christians of all denominations, whether in groups, families or as individuals who want to spend time away from it all. Healing, teaching and renewal conferences are held here, and prayer, counselling and ministry in the power of the Holy Spirit are available by arrangement. In addition there are musical concerts and exhibitions of paintings. This is very much a place for those who are already Christians and not for those who feel that the realisation of their spirituality may be obtained through other faiths.

Open: *All year. Receives men, women, young people, families, groups, non-retreatants and Christian religious.*
Rooms: *1 single, 8 doubles, dormitory.*
Facilities: *Conferences, garden, park, library, guest lounge, TV and direct-dialling pay phone. Camping site nearby. Children welcomed.*
Spiritual Help: *Personal talks, group sharing, Christian meditation, directed study.*
Guests Admitted to: *Chapel, work of the community.*
Meals: *Everyone eats together. Wholefood, with provision for vegetarian and special diets.*
Special Activities: *Planned programme of events. Send for brochure.*
Situation: *Very quiet, in the countryside.*
Maximum Stay: *By arrangement.*
Bookings: *By letter.*

Charges: *£18 per person per day half-board.*
Access: *Consult the brochure map.*

Truro

'Shalom'
23 Tresawls Avenue
Truro
Cornwall TR1 3LA   Telephone: 0872 41680

Anglican

'Shalom' is a privately owned and run large bungalow two miles from the centre of Truro. It is a peaceful base from which to explore locally, with a magnificent cathedral and National Trust gardens nearby. For those who find pets a calming influence, 'Shalom' offers two resident cats.

Open: *All year. Receives men, women, young people, families, groups, non-retreatants.*
Rooms: *1 single and 1 double, plus a child's bed.*
Facilities: *Disabled, nearby church, garden, library, TV and pay phone. Children welcomed. Dogs permitted by arrangement.*
Spiritual Help: *Personal talks, group sharing – meditation and directed study can be arranged. The sick and the elderly are welcome for spiritual healing and the laying on of hands.*
Guests Admitted to: *Unrestricted access.*
Meals: *Everyone eats together. Traditional food, with provision for vegetarian and special diets.*
Special Activities: *No planned programme of events. A peaceful setting is offered for guests to 'come and rest awhile' or to 'find' themselves.*
Situation: *Quiet bungalow $1^1/_2$ miles from Truro, near golf course.*
Maximum Stay: *By arrangement.*
Bookings: *By letter or telephone.*
Charges: *£15 per person per day.*
Access: *By rail or car to Truro.*

Buckfastleigh

Buckfast Abbey
Buckfastleigh
Devon TQ11 OEE

Telephone: 0364 43301

Roman Catholic

Over half a million people come to visit the Abbey, to walk through its grounds by the River Dart, and to admire the work of these monks whose history here has been so remarkable. The monastery was founded in 1018. It experienced centuries of peace, followed by ruin when Henry VIII dissolved the monasteries and, finally, restoration in 1907, when the monks returned to rebuild their Abbey. The great church was finished in 1937, largely restored to its original form, and filled with beautiful artefacts from the enamelled and bejewelled Stations of the Cross to the glorious marble mosaic floor of the nave. Down a nearby path, edged with pink cyclamen, stands the village of hives belonging to the Abbey's famous bees. Apart from honey, Buckfast is also well known for its herbal tonic-wine and for the creation of stained-glass windows. Yet the real work of the monks is to seek communion with God. Guests report that the food is plentiful and good. The rooms are simple and comfortable and the community friendly and very welcoming. In the dark shadows of the church the voices of the choir at morning prayer bring awareness that you have left your ordinary life and are embarking on a new journey of the spirit. **Highly Recommended.**

Open: *All year. Receives men only but there are plans to offer accommodation for women, so please enquire.*
Rooms: *10 rooms in the monastery, in the form of singles or doubles.*
Facilities: *Church, large garden, river and country walks, library by permission, bookshop and tearoom.*
Spiritual Help: *Private retreats. Guestmaster is available for help.*
Guests Admitted to: *Choir, community common-room.*
Restricted access to monastic enclosure.
Meals: *Everyone eats together in the refectory. The food is very traditional.*
Special Activities: *No planned programme.*
Situation: *Beautiful location, monastery very quiet but there are a lot of tourists in grounds and church during the day.*
Maximum Stay: *By arrangement.*
Bookings: *By letter.*
Charges: *According to means.*

Access: *BR: Newton Abbot station 11 miles away. Bus: Devon General No. 188 from Newton Abbot. Coach: National, Exeter – Plymouth. Car: via A38.*

Stoodleigh

Rainbow Sunrise
Bethlehem
3 Rainbows, Stoodleigh
Devon EX16 9QQ   Telephone: 088488 406

New Age - Yoga

Small dynamic and supportive camps in spiritual discoveries and adventures, held in areas of natural beauty. Limited to 50 adults but children may be brought and they have their own activities area. There is a wholefood cafe, workshop spaces and most facilities. Typical courses on offer are Tantra Yoga and the Vision Quest and Pipe Sharing Camp based on the Medicine Wheel Way. Charges range from £40 to £75 with special rates for children. Leaflet available.

Honiton

The Devon Vihara
Odle Cottage
Upottery
nr. Honiton
Devon EX14 9QE   Telephone: 0404 891251

Buddhist

Down a winding road and up a little hill nestles an ordinary house where the spirit of 'right-mindfulness' lives. Here a small group of mostly young monks have created a place of loving peace. This is a monastic community following the practice of the ancient forest tradition of Theravada Buddhism. They are in the middle of planting hundreds of trees so that they and others may walk and meditate among natural beauty. When I first visited, the Abbot was in the garden giving spiritual guidance to a middle-aged woman; in another spot two strapping, sun-tanned monks were chopping wood; and in another a 'learner' or novice was preparing food. Soon I was sitting in the sun sipping a glass of tea, enfolded in a happy, positive and companionable atmosphere. It is a simple place following a full monastic routine in which guests participate. Here you can meditate in the shrine room and share the common bowl of food and in the work of the community – and perhaps discover the power of inner stillness. **Highly Recommended.**

Open: *Closed throughout January and February. Receives men, women, young people, families and groups.*
Rooms: *1 double room, caravans, 2 little hermitage-huts. Everything is simple, practical and basic.*
Facilities: *Shrine room, very small tape-and-book library, common room, DIY cooking facilities, camping, garden, fields.*
Spiritual Help: *Spiritual direction, group meditation, occasional group retreats.*
Guests Admitted to: *Everywhere except monks' area. Welcome to help with work of community.*
Meals: *Usually people bring food as everyone eats together. Food is simple and almost always vegetarian.*
Special Activities: *Forest and fields used for walking and meditation. Send for brochure.*
Situation: *Buried in the Devon hills, surrounded by fields with views for miles around – delightful spot.*
Maximum Stay: *By arrangement, but first-time guests for 3 days only.*
Bookings: *By letter.*
Charges: *By donation.*
Access: *Car: take A303 towards Honiton, turn at Upottery towards Raw Ridge, turn right at Raw Ridge, follow no-through track to end – about 1 mile.*

Lynton

Lee Abbey
Lynton
North Devon EX35 6JJ   Telephone: 0598 52621

Anglican - Interdenominational

Lee Abbey is a very large country estate in the Exmoor National Park with facilities that include tennis-courts, a sports hall, and a beach and forest to explore. Lew Abbey was founded to provide a centre for the renewal of the church. While Anglican in tradition, it is ecumenical in outlook. Now run by a Christian community of about 75 men, women and families. Formal retreats are in the minority among their programmed activities, but there are what are called 'Breakaway' weeks or weekends for those who may wish to benefit from the accommodation and facilities without joining in an organised activity. Silence is not to be expected, but peace and quiet can normally be found in one or other of the several public rooms and around the gardens and parks of the estate – but there is no guarantee of this. The Abbey Fellowship includes two other communities: the Lee Abbey International Students' Club, London, and the Aston Cottage Community, Birmingham.

Open: *All year, but closed for 2 months spread over the year, so double-check. Receives men, women, young people (those under 16 to be accompanied by adults), families, groups and non-retreatants.*
Rooms: *20 singles, 36 doubles, 2 dormitories.*
Facilities: *Conferences, park, library, guest lounge, sports hall, tennis, adventure playground and pay phone. Children welcomed.*
Spiritual Help: *Teaching sessions occur each day and there is opportunity for personal talks and group sharing. No individual retreats but preached retreats are offered.*
Guests Admitted to: *Access to house and grounds, with the exception of certain areas used by the community. Chapel.*
Meals: *Everyone eats together. Traditional food with provision for vegetarian and certain special diets.*
Special Activities: *Lee Abbey has an extensive programme of activities, so do send for the brochure and magazine.*
Situation: *The house is set in a 260-acre coastal estate in the Exmoor National Park. Quiet surroundings.*
Maximum Stay: *2 weeks.*
Bookings: *By letter.*
Charges: *See brochure as these vary.*
Access: *By car is best.*

Lynton

Monastery of Poor Clares
Lynton
Devon EX35 6BX   Telephone: 0598 53373

Roman Catholic

Those who wish to share the quiet, prayer and worship of the Franciscan way of life will find a warm welcome from the sisters, whose convent in this small seaside resort is near many beauty spots on the edge of Exmoor. An ideal place for a private retreat or for those who need a very peaceful and modest base. Lovely walks by the sea.

Open: *Open April to November. Receives men (up to two at a time), women, religious sisters and young people.*

Rooms: *2-bedded self-contained flatlet, and single rooms in extern part of the monastery.*

Facilities: *Chapel, nearby beaches and moor for walking.*

Spiritual Help: *Personal talks by arrangement.*

Guests Admitted to: *Chapel, choir.*

Meals: *DIY facilities in the flat. Meals served for religious sisters in the refectory.*

Special Activities: *No planned programme.*

Situation: *A delightful area in which to retreat from the world at large.*

Maximum Stay: *4 weeks.*

Bookings: *By letter or telephone.*

Charges: *Daily rates very modest for the flat, but enquire about current prices.*

Access: *Car: via A39. BR and buses to Barnstaple, which is about 18 miles distant.*

Newton Abbot

Gaia House
Woodland Road
Denbury
nr. Newton Abbot
Devon TQ12 6DY   Telephone: 0803 813188

Buddhist - Non-denominational

While those going on personal retreat at Gaia House will need to have practised insight meditation, known as Vipassana Meditation, for at least six months already, group retreats are scheduled throughout the year and there is guided meditation for beginners. Associated with the Sharpham North Community, the house maintains silence except at times of teaching so retreatants conduct their stay at Gaia House in silence unless meeting with the teacher or for group interviews. There is a daily one hour work period in which all join.

Open: *All year. Receives men and women.*

Rooms: *5 singles, 3 doubles, dormitory.*
Facilities: *Meditation room, park, garden, library, guest lounge, and pay phone.*
Spiritual Help: *Meditation, group sharing and personal talks with meditation teachers, group and personal retreats.*
Guests Admitted to: *Unrestricted access everywhere except kitchen area.*
Meals: *Everyone eats together. All food is vegetarian.*
Special Activities: *Planned programme. Send for brochure.*
Situation: *Very quiet, in the countryside.*
Maximum Stay: *6 months, with permission.*
Bookings: *By letter.*
Charges: *See brochure.*
Access: *By car is best.*

Totnes

The Barn
Lower Sharpham Barton
Ashprington
Totnes
Devon TQ9 7DX   Telephone: 0803 732661

Buddhist – Inter-faith

During your stay here, you will be expected to be fully involved in the daily schedule of activities and to take your turn preparing vegetarian meals for everyone. One evening a week is devoted to discussing personal matters as well as broader issues that relate to the community's life together. You are encouraged to pursue those activities – such as Buddhist-study classes, yoga mornings, and listening to cassettes of Dharma talks – which support a contemplative way of life. The Sharpham North Community is a short walk away across fields and you can participate in their wider range of lectures and events, but you will find only limited opportunity to stray outside the Sharpham Estate because of community commitments there. Considering that the daily schedule includes four to five hours' work on the land and three 45-minute periods of group meditation, this hardly comes as a surprise. If you are reasonably fit, then have a 'go' at this farming retreat community, where you will find the usual warm Buddhist welcome. **Highly Recommended.**

Open: *All year. Receives men and women – you do not have to be a*

Buddhist, but an established background in meditation is necessary.
Rooms: *7 singles.*
Facilities: *Garden, library and pay phone. Woodworking equipment is provided.*
Spiritual Help: *Personal talks when a teacher is available, group sharing and meditation. The community offers a supportive environment with regular weekly visits from local meditation teachers, who also provide one-to-one meetings.*
Guests Admitted to: *Unrestricted access to all areas, including shrineroom and work of the community, which consists of gardening, woodland maintenance, household care and upkeep, cooking, preserving, looking after poultry.*
Meals: *Everyone eats together. Meals consist of vegetarian wholefood. Special diets if required.*
Special Activities: *Daily schedule followed 6 days a week.*
Situation: *Very quiet and in the countryside. Beautiful location on the Sharpham Estate, on a hillside overlooking the River Dart – no roads visible.*
Maximum Stay: *6 months (minimum is 1 week).*
Bookings: *By letter or telephone, but you will be asked for some personal details about your experience of retreat and meditation.*
Charges: *£8 per day up to 2 weeks, £7 per day from 2 weeks to 2 months stay, over 2 months it is £6 per day. Those with low income pay £6 per day.*
Access: *By car is best, but enquire if you want to walk from the nearest place served by public transport.*

Totnes

The Dartington Centre
Dartington Hall
Totnes
Devon TQ9 6EL   Telephone: 0803 862271

Non-religious, non-sectarian

The Dartington Hall Trust has been going for 60 years, giving focus and support to a variety of activities connected with education, research, business and the arts. Dartington Hall is part of a busy estate that comprises famous educational colleges in the arts and music, together with tourist attractions such as a cider-press centre and a craft shop. The Centre itself is predominantly a place for conferences, but individuals are welcome to stay. It is perhaps not a place that permits a total escape from ordinary life, but courses on meditation are available. And, indeed, who can say that you will not find the course on lace-making or Indian music to be just the right introduction to a quieter look at what you are doing with your life?

Open: *All year. Receives men, women, young people, families, groups and non-retreatants.*
Rooms: *40 singles, 10 doubles.*
Facilities: *Limited disabled, conferences, garden, library, guest lounge and pay phone.*
Spiritual Help: *Directed study.*
Guests Admitted to: *Most areas of Centre and grounds.*
Meals: *Everyone eats together. Traditional wholefood, with provision for vegetarian and special diets.*
Special Activities: *Planned programme of events. Send for brochure.*
Situation: *Very quiet, in the countryside. Dartington Hall is a medieval manor-house set in a courtyard, with extensive gardens and grounds.*
Maximum Stay: *Unlimited.*
Bookings: *By letter or telephone.*
Charges: *Available on request.*
Access: *By rail or car.*

Totnes

Oakwood Retreats
The Old Postern
Dartington
Totnes, Devon TQ9 6EA   Telephone: 0803 865934

Non-religious

Oakwood relies on no religious tradition and provides retreats in the context of reducing stress, finding greater clarity of purpose, reconciling personal and business values, and helping to create greater awareness and wiser decision making. They are run by Dr. Guy Claxton who is a visiting professor at the University of Bristol. The Old Postern is a secluded 14th century manor house set in its own grounds on the Dartington Hall Estate. Woodlands, meadows and river walks are all nearby.

Open: *On announced retreat dates. Receives men, women, young*

people, families, and groups.
Rooms: *20 singles, 4 doubles.*
Facilities: *Garden, park, library, and pay phone.*
Spiritual Help: *Personal talks, group sharing, meditation, directed study.*
Guests Admitted to: *Unrestricted access, work of community.*
Meals: *Everyone eats together. Vegetarian only.*
Special Activities: *Planned programme of events. Send for brochure.*
Situation: *Very quiet in the countryside.*
Maximum Stay: *6 days.*
Bookings: *By letter.*
Charges: *Varies according to programme but a guideline would be £145 to £245 for the week for a person paying themselves. Ask for current tariff.*
Access: *By rail to Totnes or by car.*

Totnes

Sharpham North Community
Ashprington
Totnes
Devon TQ9 7UT   Telephone: 080423 542

Buddhist – Non-denominational

Sharpham House is a beautiful English Palladian building with views stretching down to the River Dart. It is here that the Sharpham Trust strives to create a new way of life, aiming to achieve a balance between the practical and the spiritual. Occupying part of the house is the Community, which comprises up to nine people from different backgrounds and nationalities who share a common interest in spiritual practice and its application to daily life. Although the approach is Buddhist, it does not adhere to any particular school. The programme is one that combines meditation with talks and recitals. These are broadly based and might range from a talk on the creation of a greener world by Satish Kumar, editor of *Resurgence* magazine, to a discourse on the art of giving by a teacher of insight meditation from New York or to an evening of Russian music and poetry.

Open: *February to July. Closed January and August. Receives men, women and young people.*
Rooms: *2 singles, dormitories, and hermitage room.*

Facilities: *Park, garden, library, phone. No smoking permitted in the house.*
Spiritual Help: *Personal talks, meditation, group sharing, directed study.*
Guests Admitted to: *Shrine room, work of community.*
Meals: *Everyone eats together. Meals consist of vegetarian wholefood.*
Special Activities: *2 residential group retreats per year, lasting a weekend each. All guests are expected to participate in the life and work of the community (including approximately 2 hours' gardening and cleaning and 2 hours' meditation daily). Send for the brochure of events.*
Situation: *Very quiet, but a busy and active place.*
Maximum Stay: *3 days.*
Bookings: *By letter; all overnight stays must be booked in advance.*
Charges: *Suggested minimum donation £3 per night plus some participation each day in community work.*
Access: *BR to Totnes, then by car or on foot.*

DORSET

Bridport

Monkton Wyld Court
Charmouth
Bridport
Dorset DT6 6DQ   Telephone: 0297 60342

New Age

Eleven acres of grounds surround this large Victorian rectory that is situated in a secluded valley on the Devon–Dorset border. Monkton is a leading New Age centre for holistic education run by a community of 11 adults plus children. The emphasis is on encouraging personal and spiritual growth, combined with a firm commitment to 'green' issues and self-sufficiency. There are plenty of courses that reflect this approach. These include a weekend for women to develop their skills in creativity and healing, and instruction in breathing practices, T'ai Ch'i therapy, and transformative arts incorporating contemporary Shamanism.

Open: *All year except Christmas. Receives men, women, young people, families and groups.*
Rooms: *3 doubles, 2 dormitories, 6 rooms each sleeping 3 people.*

Facilities: *For conferences, arts and crafts and pottery. There is also an organic garden, library, guest lounge, meditation room and pay phone. Children welcomed.*
Spiritual Help: *Personal talks, meditation.*
Guests Admitted to: *Work of the community.*
Meals: *Everyone eats together. Wholefood, with provision for vegetarian and special diets.*
Special Activities: *Planned programme of events. Send for brochure.*
Situation: *Very quiet, in the countryside.*
Maximum Stay: *5 days.*
Bookings: *By letter or telephone.*
Charges: *£85 programme weekend.*
Access: *By rail or car (A35).*

Dorchester

Society of St Francis
Hilfield Friary
Hilfield
nr. Dorchester
Dorset DT2 7BE   Telephone: 0300 341345

Anglican

It is up to each guest to decide how best to use his or her time at the Friary, but all are welcome to join the brothers in chapel for prayer. Set in peaceful surroundings, this is a quiet community where you will find space for thinking things through. Many guests have busy and active careers, and find that the Friary is just the place they need for rest and reflection. Hospitality is offered to all, so you may find that the man at prayer next to you could equally well be a successful industrialist or a wayfarer who tramps the road.

Open: *All year from Tuesdays to Saturdays, except mid-July to end August. Receives men, women, young people, groups and non-retreatants.*
Rooms: *13 singles, 1 double.*
Facilities: *Chapel, oratory, choir, garden, library, a book and craft shop, guest lounge and pay phone. Bring a towel.*
Spiritual Help: *Personal talks and group sharing.*
Guests Admitted to: *Chapel, choir and work of the community but not to novices' house, monks' enclosure or Bernard House unless*

received there.

Meals: *Everyone eats together. Traditional food, with provision for vegetarian and special diets, if notification given in advance.*

Special Activities: *Planned programme. Send for brochure.*

Situation: *Very quiet, in the countryside; modern guest-house situated on what was once a farm.*

Maximum Stay: *6 days.*

Bookings: *By letter.*

Charges: *By donation – about £14 per day as a guideline.*

Access: *BR to Dorchester. Guests can be met at the station, but please do make a donation towards such costs.*

Poole

Post Green Pastoral Centre
56 Dorchester Road
Lytchett Minster
Poole
Dorset BH16 6JE   Telephone: 0202 622510

Ecumenical

This is a community made up of people who are committed to live a life of faith combined with a concern for the spiritual healing of both individuals and society. They include married couples, families and single people, all of whom are involved at the Centre. The counselling available can help you to make important choices and decisions, and to grow towards taking full responsibility for your own life in a creative way.

Open: *All year, except Christmas. Receives men, women, young people, groups and non-retreatants.*

Rooms: *Both singles and double are available.*

Facilities: *Small conferences, garden, library, guest lounge, TV and direct-dialling telephone. Spring Bank Holiday.*

Spiritual Help: *Personal talks, meditation, directed study, group sharing on residential courses, counselling, spiritual direction and various teaching courses. A silent retreat is possible.*

Guests Admitted to: *Chapel, work of the community.*

Meals: *Everyone eats together. Traditional food with provision for vegetarian and special diets.*

Special Activities: *Planned retreats and courses. Send for brochure.*

Situation: *Quiet open countryside nearby. The Centre overlooks*

Poole Harbour.
Maximum Stay: *By arrangement, but can vary from 1 night to a year.*
Bookings: *By letter or telephone.*
Charges: *Vary according to course and counselling – see brochure.*
Access: *BR: to Poole. Bus: to Lytchett Minster every hour. Car: via A350 to B3067.*

Wimborne

Ashton Lodge
Stanbridge
Wimborne
Dorset BH12 4JO　　　　　Telephone: 0202 841522

Non-denominational – Spiritual

This is a small retreat-house with a farm, school and a conference centre. Retreat visitors here can use the Gaunts House sanctuary and study centre, which is about a mile and a half away.

Open: *All year. Receives men, women, young people, and groups.*
Rooms: *12 rooms, 12 doubles.*
Facilities: *Conferences, chapel, shrineroom, garden, park, camping and caravan site, guest lounge, TV and pay phone. Children welcomed. No pets.*
Spiritual Help: *Personal talks, group sharing, meditation, directed study, counselling.*
Guests Admitted to: *Unrestricted access, work of community.*
Meals: *Wholefood with vegetarians and special diets catered for.*
Special Activities: *Planned programme at Gaunts House which retreat guests are welcome to attend. Send for brochure.*
Situation: *Very quiet, in the countryside.*
Maximum Stay: *Unlimited - but minimum stay is 2 nights.*
Bookings: *By letter or telephone.*
Charges: *£15 B&B.*
Access: *BR: Poole. Car: Centre is 3 miles north of Wimborne Minster.*

'Happiness cannot be found through great effort and willpower,
but is already there, in relaxation and letting go.'

Ven. Lama Gendun Rinpoche

Wimborne

Gaunts House
Wimborne
Dorset BH21 4JQ   Telephone: 0202 841522

Non-denominational - Spiritual

Part of the Gaunts estate and dedicated to the development of life on a spiritual basis. It offers space and help for spiritual and personal development with a supportive community, all set in beautiful parkland.

Open: *All year. Receives men, women, young people, families, and groups.*
Rooms: *4 singles, 3 doubles.*
Facilities: *Conferences, camping, garden, park, library, guest lounge, TV and pay phone. Children welcomed. No pets.*
Spiritual Help: *Personal talks, group sharing, meditation, support and advice, counselling if required.*
Guests Admitted to: *Unrestricted access to all areas including chapel, shrine room, work of the community.*
Meals: *Vegetarian - guests share the cooking. Food may be brought or purchased there. Provision for special diets if necessary.*
Special Activities: *None.*
Situation: *Very quiet in the countryside.*
Maximum Stay: *Unlimited.*
Bookings: *By letter or telephone.*
Charges: *About £37.50 a night or £70 per person/week plus VAT.*
Access: *BR to Poole. Bus to Wimborne, then taxi or telephone for a lift.*

Wimborne

High Lea
Hinton Martell
Wimborne
Dorset BH21 5AA   Telephone: 0202 841522

Non-denominational - Spiritual

Part of the Gounts estate which is for major retreat groups.

Open: *All year. Receives men, women and groups.*

Rooms: *3 doubles, dormitories, camping site.*
Facilities: *Conferences, camping, garden, park, guest lounge, pay phone. Children welcomed. No pets.*
Spiritual Help: *Group sharing, meditation, directed study, support and advice. Counselling if required.*
Guests Admitted to: *Unrestricted access, chapel, shrine room, work of community.*
Meals: *Everyone eats together. Wholefood, provision for vegetarians.*
Special Activities: *None - but some are planned, so enquire.*
Situation: *Very quiet in countryside.*
Maximum Stay: *By arrangement.*
Bookings: *By letter or telephone.*
Charges: *£7.50 per night plus VAT*
Access: *BR to Poole. Bus to Wimborne, then taxi or telephone for a lift.*

Wimborne

Hinton Retreat
Hinton Parva
Wimborne
Dorset BH21 4JG   Telephone: 0202 841522

Non-denominational - Spiritual

A large private estate dedicated to the development of life on a spiritual basis. It offers space and help for spiritual, environmental, healing, and personal development.

Open: *All year. Receives men, women, young people, families, groups, and non-retreatants.*
Rooms: *40 singles, 8 doubles. Can sleep up to 120 people.*
Facilities: *Disabled, conferences, chapel, shrine room, study centre, garden, park, camping and caravan site, library, guest lounge, TV and pay phone. Children welcomed. No pets.*
Spiritual Help: *Personal talks, group sharing, meditation, directed study*
Guests Admitted to: *Unrestricted access to all areas including chapel, shrine room, work of the community.*
Meals: *Everyone eats together. Wholefood with good vegetarian dishes. Provision for special diets.*
Special Activities: *Planned programme of events. Send for brochure.*

Situation: *Very quiet*
Maximum Stay: *5 weeks*
Bookings: *By letter or telephone.*
Charges: *£70 per week plus VAT- about £7.50 per day.*
Access: *BR: to Poole. Bus: Wimborne, then taxi or telephone.*

SOMERSET

Castle Cary

St John's Priory
Victoria Road
Castle Cary
Somerset BA7 7DF   Telephone: 0963 50429

Roman Catholic

The guest house at St John's sits behind a little orchard of trees, and the chapel is small and friendly. Guests are not usually accepted just for overnight visits. Bring soap and a hot water bottle if you normally use one in winter.

Open: *All year except Christmas. Receives women, clergy, couples, groups, non-retreatants.*
Rooms: *6 singles, 2 doubles.*
Facilities: *Chapel, garden, guest lounge, TV. No guest phone. No pets.*
Spiritual Help: *The sisters do not conduct retreats themselves, but some are available for a 'chat' about prayer and meditation.*
Guests Admitted to: *Chapel.*
Meals: *Taken in the guest house. Traditional food for lunch and supper with self-catering for breakfast. No provision for vegetarians or special diets.*
Special Activities: *Everyone is welcome to join the sisters in the celebration of the Eucharist and the Divine Office.*
Situation: *Very quiet, in the countryside.*
Maximum Stay: *3 weeks.*
Bookings: *By letter.*
Charges: *Single room £18 per day, double room £34 per day. Weekly rate : £24 single, £236 double.*
Access: *BR: Castle Cary. Buses: from Shepton Mallet or Yeovil. Car: M3 Exit 8.*

Glastonbury

Abbey House
Chilkwell Street
Glastonbury
Somerset BA6 8DH   Telephone: 0458 831112

Anglican

This is the Bath and Wells Retreat and Conference House, which is set in 40 acres of beautiful parkland right in the town centre. There is no community or staff here as a lay team manages the place. The great majority of the guests are sponsored by religious and church groups but private retreatants are welcomed and often can be accommodated at short notice if only a small group is in residence at the time. While activities are mostly aimed at group retreats, there are plenty of workshops, talks and events which individuals attend on their own. It is an interesting place and always worth a try.

Open: *All year except late August to mid-September. Receives men and women.*
Rooms: *17 singles and 8 twin-bedded rooms.*
Facilities: *Garden, park, library, guest lounge, payphone.*
Spiritual Help: *Groups bring their own leaders. There is no resident pastoral staff.*
Guests Admitted to: *Unrestricted access.*
Meals: *Wholefood with provision for vegetarians and special diets.*
Special Activities: *Conferences, day meetings and visits from parish parties. See brochure.*
Situation: *In town, but in a parkland setting near abbey ruins.*
Maximum Stay: *7 days.*
Bookings: *By letter or telephone.*
Charges: *See the brochure.*
Access: *BR: nearest railway station is Castle Cary (15 miles). Bus: Badgerline No. 376 travels hourly at 5 minutes to the hour from Bristol coach station; National Express coach runs daily from London Victoria.*

Glastonbury

Self Realisation Healing Centre
Laurel Lane
Queen Camel
Glastonbury
Somerset BA22 7NU   Telephone: 0935 850266

New Age - Nondenominational

The Centre is a charitable trust run by a team of counsellors and healers living and working together as a family using the guidance of yoga and healing creative self-development. A 17th century house with extensive grounds and offering plenty of space and facilities, including a therapy pool. It is set within its own grounds near the River Cam and open countryside. The ancient spiritual centres of Glastonbury and Wells are within easy reach.

Open: *All year. Receives men, women, young people, families, groups and non-retreatants.*
Rooms: *5 singles, 4 doubles plus other available sleeping space.*
Facilities: *Meditation room, garden, library, guest lounge and pay phone. Children welcome.*
Spiritual Help: *Personal talks, meditation courses and guidance, directed study, healing, progressive counselling, yoga, spiritual self-development, training and guidance in healing instruction.*
Guests Admitted to: *Unrestricted access to all areas, including meditation room and therapy swimming work.*
Meals: *Served to individual needs, with wholefood and provision for vegetarian and special diets.*
Special Activities: *This is a 'Self-realisation Centre' with a planned programme, so send for the brochure. The centre arranges individual tuition and training wherever required, together with courses and workshops additional to the scheduled programme.*
Situation: *Very quiet, in the village. Within easy reach of Glastonbury, Wells, Bath, Bristol and Yeovil.*
Maximum Stay: *By arangement.*
Bookings: *By letter or telephone.*
Charges: *See programme.*
Access: *Car: via A303. Collecting service from the nearest BR stations.*

Heddington

International Meditaton Centre
The Sayagyi U Ba Khin Memorial Trust
Splatts House
Heddington, Calne
Wiltshire SN11 OPE   Telephone: 0380 850238

Buddhist (Theravadian)

Established for some thirteen years, the International Meditation Centre provides for the instruction and practice of the Theravada Buddhist meditation, guided by two disciples who have practised and taught meditation for more than thirty-five years. Ten- day residential courses are held twice each month.

Open: *All year. Receives men and women.*
Rooms: *Various rooms available.*
Facilities: *Light of the Dhamma Pagoda.*
Spiritual Help: *Meditation.*
Guests Admitted to: *Unrestricted access to most areas.*
Meals: *Everyone eats together. Vegetarian food. Special diets will be accommodated as far as possible..*
Special Activities: *Planned programme of events. Send for brochure.*
Situation: *Quiet on edge of a village.*
Maximum Stay: *By arrangement.*
Bookings: *By letter.*
Charges: *Contribution toward food and accommodation.*
Access: *Rail, bus, and car all possible. See brochure.*

Warminster

St Denys Retreat Centre
2 Church Street
Warminster
Wilts. BA12 8PG   Telephone: 0985 214824

Anglican

This is an attractive house set right on the street, but there is a garden. The community offers individual retreats in the Ignatian tradition as well as 'walk-into-quietness days' when a team of sisters welcome you to a day retreat in the centre. Well organised and friendly.

Open: *All year except part of January. Receives men, women, young people, groups and non-retreatants.*
Rooms: *16 singles, 6 doubles.*
Facilities: *Disabled, conferences, chapel, garden, library, guest lounge and guest telephone.*
Spiritual Help: *Personal talks, meditation, individually guided retreats.*
Guests Admitted to: *Unrestricted access to all areas, including chapel.*
Meals: *Everyone eats together. Traditional food – vegetarian and special diets can be catered for with advance notification.*
Special Activities: *Planned programme of events. Send for brochure.*
Situation: *Quiet, in the town.*
Maximum Stay: *2 weeks.*
Bookings: *By telephone, but confirm by letter.*
Charges: *£18 per person per day.*
Access: *BR: Portsmouth – Cardiff line. Bus: from Salisbury, Bath or Towbridge. Car: via B3414, off A36.*

CHANNEL ISLANDS

Jersey

FCJ Centre of Spirituality
Deloraine Road
St Saviour
Jersey JE2 7NF   Telephone: 0534 26162

Roman Catholic – Ecumenical

The sisters of the Order of the Faithful Companions of Jesus offer individually directed retreats, prayer workshops, parenting programmes, and retreats from daily life.

Open: *All year except July, August, Christmas and Easter. Receives men, women, and young people and groups on a day basis only.*
Rooms: *10 singles.*
Facilities: *Garden and library.*
Spiritual Help: *Personal talks, group sharing, meditation, directed study.*
Guests Admitted to: *Chapel.*
Meals: *Small dining-room for retreatants. Traditional food, with provision for special diets.*

Special Activities: *No planned programme.*
Situation: *Quiet, near to a school.*
Maximum Stay: *According to length of retreat.*
Bookings: *By letter or telephone.*
Charges: *On application.*
Access: *By ferry/air.*

'Try to spread your loving mind and heart to all that they may have peace and happiness in their lives' – Ven. Dhammavijitha Thera

East & East Anglia

Biggleswade

Yoga for Health Foundation
Ickwell Bury
Biggleswade
Bedfordshire SG18 9EF   Telephone: 0767 627271

Yoga - Non-religious

The Foundation, a charity operating in many parts of the world, is in what must be the last unspoiled bit of this commuter-belt county. A 17th-century manor and farm, it is surrounded by parkland, has fine gardens, and a fishing lake left over from the Middle Ages when an abbey occupied the site. Inside the house all is different and a B&B atmosphere prevails, but the food is excellent with much that is home-produced. There are nursing staff and the place is well equipped for the disabled. Yoga training, reflexology and Swedish massage are available. All this may make it sound like a clinic, but it is far more a place where people share and grow in strength together. The health benefits of regular yoga practice, particularly for those suffering from stress, are well established.

Open: *All year except over Christmas. Receives men, women, young people, families, groups, non-retreatants.*
Rooms: *17 doubles.*
Facilities: *Excellent for disabled, gardens, park, library to be opened soon, guest lounge and pay phone. Camping and caravans by arangement. Guide dogs only.*
Spiritual Help: *Complete range of yoga technique training and activities. Personal talks, group sharing, meditation.*
Guests Admitted to: *Unrestricted access.*
Meals: *Everyone eats together. Vegetarian wholefood only. Small charge for special diets.*
Special Activities: *Send for programme of events, which includes a 10-day festival specifically for families.*
Situation: *Peaceful, in countryside – setting is hard to fault.*
Maximum Stay: *By arrangement.*
Bookings: *By telephone or letter.*
Charges: *£247 per person per week, £72.50 per weekend, £39 for 24-hour stay. Ask what is included in these charges when you enquire about booking.*
Access: *BR: to Biggleswade then by taxi. Buses: coach to Bedford. Local bus runs twice a day. Car: via A1 to Biggleswade.*

Turvey

Monastery of Christ Our Saviour
Abbey Mews
Turvey
Bedfordshire MK43 8DH   Telephone: 0234 881211

Roman Catholic

This is one of two Benedictine communities at Turvey who worship in common and work in close co-operation. The monks' guest house has been converted from a stone barn. The rooms are spacious and comfortable with a lots of books to read, an easy chair in every room and a guest kitchen. This can be a busy place but it is one where personal silence is very much respected. If you are on a private retreat, you will be left in peace to get on with it. As it is a small community, help in the garden is usually welcomed. The life here is deliberately kept simple - organic gardening, tomato growing, jam making, producing small pottery objects and cooking delicious wholefood dishes are some of the specialities of the monks. **Highly Recommended.**

Open: *All year except Christmas. Receives men, women, young people, families, groups and non-retreatants.*
Rooms: *4 singles, 1 double.*
Facilities: *Small meetings, garden, library, fields in which to walk, guest lounge and pay phone. Children and pets welcomed.*
Spiritual Help: *Participation in the liturgy.*
Guests Admitted to: *Chapel, choir, and some work of the community.*
Meals: *Taken in the guest house. Excellent wholefood with self-catering available. Provision for vegetarians and special diets. Much of the food is organic and grown by the monks.*
Special Activities: *No planned programme of events. Attached to the guesthouse but quite separate is the Turvey Centre for Group Therapy, a partnership of one of the monks, two psychiatrists and a psychotherapist, all of whom are members of the Institute of Group Analysis. The centre provides individual and group psychotherapy for people in need regardless of their religious orientation. There is also a pastoral work group for people engaged in pastoral work within religious organisations. In conjunction with the University of Warwick, the Centre offers training in group-psychotherapy. (Telephone 0234 888952 for further information about the Centre)*
Situation: *The village has a lot of traffic, but the guest house and gardens are quiet.*

Maximum Stay: *To be agreed according to each particular case.*
Bookings: *By letter or telephone.*
Charges: *Donations accepted.*
Access: *BR: to Bedford or Northampton, then by local bus. Car: via M1, Exit 14 to Olney.*

Turvey

Priory of Our Lady of Peace
Turvey Abbey
Turvey
Bedfordshire MK43 8DE   Telephone: 0234 881432

Roman Catholic

Although the Abbey is next to a busy road, the sisters have created an oasis of peace in this picturesque stone village by the River Ouse. The modern guest house is warm and the bedrooms are well-appointed and light. There is a garden in which to sit, while the grounds offer good walks through Abbey Park and beyond to open fields. Guests do not have to join the daily offices of prayer but the beautifully sung liturgy helps immeasurably in the quietening of mind and body and in the opening of the heart. The meals are excellent with home-baked bread and usually a delicious pudding. The programme of events is very popular. There is an annual summer event for men and women under forty to join the community in a week of living the Benedictine monastic life. **Highly Recommended.**

Open: *All year, except January and September. Receives men, women, young people, families, groups, non-retreatants.*
Rooms: *16 singles, doubles available.*
Facilities: *Small conferences, garden, library, guest lounge and pay phone. There are some days especially for mothers with young children. No pets.*
Spiritual Help: *Guests are welcome to join in the Divine Office and are provided with books. From time to time introductory talks are given to help people participate more deeply. Daily Mass. Personal talks, meditation, and prayer guidance.*
Guests Admitted to: *Chapel, occasionally work of the community.*
Meals: *Meals are taken in guest house area. Food is more or less traditional with some wholefood dishes. With advance notice, provision can be made for vegetarian and special diets. Self-catering available.*

Special Activities: *Planned programme of events. Send for brochure.*
Situation: *In the village near countryside with fields to the rear and side.*
Maximum Stay: *2 weeks, with some exceptions.*
Bookings: *Preferably by letter.*
Charges: *£16 per person per day full board. Weekends £50 inclusive.*
Access: *BR: to Bedford or Northampton and then bus to Turvey. Car: via A428.*

CAMBRIDGESHIRE

Cambridge

Sisters of the Adoration Convent
17 Glisson Road
Cambridge CB1 2HA   Telephone: (Ex-directory)

Roman Catholic

The Sisters of the Adoration are a very small contemplative community and have only one single room available for women guests. There may be no limit here to the warmth of their welcome – but lots of letters can mean too much work for too few hands. So try to decide why you want to make a retreat here before enquiring, and remember to send an s.a.e. This kind of small community is often best suited to those who have already been on retreat elsewhere and may be now considering a religious vocation.

Open: *All year except Holy Week and Christmas. Receives women on retreat only.*
Rooms: *1 single.*
Facilities: *Library, the sisters' quiet lounge.*
Spiritual Help: *Personal talks, meditation, and sometimes group sharing. The special mission of the sisters is 'Eucharistic Adoration', in the sense of acquired knowledge, appreciation and meditation. Mass is held in the nearby parish church.*
Guests Admitted to: *Chapel.*
Meals: *Everyone eats together or in guest house. Traditional food.*
Special Activities: *No planned programme of events.*
Situation: *Rather busy, in the city.*
Maximum Stay: *8 days.*
Bookings: *By letter only.*

Charges: *By donation.*
Access: *By rail to Cambridge. Local buses are available.*

Ely

Bishop Woodford House
Barton Road
Ely
Cambs. CB7 4DX   Telephone: 0353 663039

Anglican – Ecumenical

Open: *All year. Receives men, women, young people, families, groups , religious, and non-retreatants.*
Rooms: *34 singles.*
Facilities: *Disabled (ground floor bedrooms and W.C.), conferences, chapel, garden, nearby park, library, guest lounge, TV and guest telephone. Children welcome.*
Spiritual Help: *Personal talks, group sharing, meditation, directed study, with ministers and counsellors available as required.*
Guests Admitted to: *Unrestricted access everywhere.*
Meals: *Everyone eats in the dining room. Traditional and wholefood with provision for vegetarian and special diets.*
Special Activities: *Some planned events – brochure available.*
Situation: *Quiet on the outskirts of the city.*
Maximum Stay: *30 days.*
Bookings: *By telephone or letter.*
Charges: *£23.50 per person full board.*
Access: *By rail, bus to Ely. Car: A10*

Huntingdon

Community of the Resurrection
St Francis House
Hemingford Grey
Huntingdon
Cambs. PE18 9BJ   Telephone: 0480 462185

Anglican

Renovated a few years ago, St Francis House is designed for retreatants and the aim is to maintain a peaceful atmosphere at all times.

Although the house is in the village, there is a large garden and you can walk beside the nearby river and through the meadows.

Open: *All year except August, Christmas, and Easter.*
Rooms: *17 singles, 3 twin-bedded rooms.*
Facilities: *Disabled, garden, guest lounge, library, pay phone.*
Spiritual Help: *Peaceful atmosphere and retreatants may talk personally with the retreat conductor.*
Guests Admitted to: *Unrestricted access.*
Meals: *Everyone eats together – traditional food with provision for vegetarians and special diets by arrangement.*
Special Activities: *Send for current retreat list.*
Situation: *Quiet, and in a picturesque village.*
Maximum Stay: *See current retreat list.*
Bookings: *By letter or telephone.*
Charges: *Available on application.*
Access: *Car: via A604.*

Peterborough

Society of the Precious Blood
St Pega's Hermitage
Peakirk
Peterborough
Cambs. PE6 7NP   Telephone: 0733 252219

Anglican

This is a small, enclosed community of nuns. It is best suited for a private, mostly silent retreat, bearing in mind that in such a place you will find a great degree of stillness and will be left on your own.

Open: *All year. Receives men, women and young people.*
Rooms: *2 singles.*
Facilities: *Garden.*
Spiritual Help: *Personal talks, some small group sharing.*
Guests Admitted to: *Chapel.*
Meals: *Served in your room. Vegetarians can be catered for.*
Special Activities: *No planned programme of events.*
Situation: *In the village. On an RAF flight path, but not unduly noisy. Adjoining the Peakirk Wildfowl Wetlands Trust.*
Maximum Stay: *1 week.*
Bookings: *By letter*

Charges: *By donation.*
Access: *BR: Peterborough station is 7 miles away. Bus or taxi from there but check first. Car: via A15.*

Chelmsford

Brentwood Diocesan Pastoral Centre
Newhall
Boreham
Chelmsford
Essex CM3 3HT   Telephone: 0245 467588

Roman Catholic – Ecumenical

Open: *All year. Receives men, women , young people, and groups.*
Rooms: *9 singles, 4 doubles.*
Facilities: *Conferences, camping, garden, park, library, guest lounge, TV and pay phone.*
Spiritual Help: *Individual spiritual direction and counselling, group sharing, meditation.*
Guests Admitted to: *Access to mainly non-residential areas. Chapel.*
Meals: *Traditional, with provision for vegetarians and special diets.*
Special Activities: *Those staying can share in the common prayer of the resident religious community. There is a very extensive pro-gramme of events, so send for brochure.*
Situation: *Quiet, in the countryside.*
Maximum Stay: *1 month.*
Bookings: *By letter or telephone.*
Charges: *Full board and lodging according to the programme course on offer.*
Access: *BR and coaches to Chelmsford, local buses.*

Chelmsford

Diocesan Retreat House
The Street
Pleshey
Chelmsford
Essex CM3 1HA   Telephone: 0245 37251

Anglican

The House of Retreat is mostly used by parish groups; individuals are welcome when there is room. A good range of weekend courses is available, ranging from an introduction to the John Main method of meditation, to instruction about how to breathe and use the body most effectively when you have embarked on the journey of prayer. It has been called 'the new Jerusalem just off the M25'.

Open: *Most of the year. Receives men, women, young people, and groups.*
Rooms: *22 singles, 2 doubles, ground-floor bedroom for the disabled. There is also a cottage in the grounds.*
Facilities: *Garden, library, day conferences, guest lounge and pay phone.*
Spiritual Help: *Personal talks, occasional group sharing, meditation, directed study. The retreats here cater for widely differing spiritual needs.*
Guests Admitted to: *Unrestricted access. Chapel.*
Meals: *Everyone eats together. Traditional food, with provision for vegetarian by prior arrangement. Self-catering in the cottage.*
Special Activities: *Quiet days, children's days, course for spiritual directors – send for the leaflet.*
Situation: *Quiet, in historic Essex village in countryside.*
Maximum Stay: *8 days.*
Bookings: *By telephone or letter.*
Charges: *On application.*
Access: *BR/bus: to Chelmsford. Car: via M11.*

There are two ways to go about getting enough – one is to continue to accumulate more and more. The other is to desire less'
– G. K. Chesterton

Ingatestone

Family Ministry of West Ham Central Mission
Bodley House
Stock Road
Stock
nr. Ingatestone
Essex CM4 9DH　　　　　　　　Telephone: 0277 840668

Baptist

This is a modern bungalow in a quiet garden, catering for day retreats
and group meetings. Bodley House works with local churches and it
is worth writing to ask what courses are planned. There is no
residential accommodation available.

Open: *All year. Receives men and women.*
Rooms: *For day conferences only.*
Facilities: *Disabled, garden, lounge.*
Spiritual Help: *None.*
Guests Admitted to: *Most of the centre, grounds.*
Meals: *DIY.*
Special Activities: *Special courses on pastoral guidance.*
Situation: *Quiet, in countryside.*
Maximum Stay: *For the day.*
Bookings: *Apply to secretary.*
Charges: *By donation.*
Access: *BR: Billericay. Buses: Nos. 152, 153 to Stock. Car: via
B1007.*

HERTFORDSHIRE

Barnet

Poor Clare Monastery
102 Galley Lane
Arkley
Barnet
Herts. EN5 4AN　　　　　　　　Telephone: 081 449 8815

Roman Catholic

The sisters live an enclosed, contemplative life, and the Monastery is open to people only on recommendation. This is a place for contemplative silence and prayer so before you ask to stay please know why you want to stay here rather than somewhere which is geared to retreats.

Open: *All year. Receives women and young people, men only occasionally.*
Rooms: *1 single room and 2 doubles available in the guest house.*
Facilities: *Chapel and garden.*
Spiritual Help: *Participation in the Divine Office.*
Guests Admitted to: *Chapel.*
Meals: *Meals taken in the guest house. Traditional food with provision for vegetarians by arrangement.*
Special Activities: *No planned programme.*
Situation: *Quiet, on edge of a village.*
Maximum Stay: *8 days.*
Bookings: *By letter.*
Charges: *By donation.*
Access: *Bus/Car: to Barnet.*

Hemel Hempstead

Amaravati Buddhist Centre
Great Gaddesden
Hemel Hempstead
Herts. HP1 3BZ   Telephone: 0442 843239

Buddhist

This is a residence for Buddhist monks and nuns of the Theravada tradition, but people of any or no formal religious affiliation are welcomed. Retreats are held in separate facilities away from the often busy life of the Amaravati community. Accommodation is basic in the dormitories, so bring a warm sleeping-bag, a blanket for use during meditation, and a towel and soap. Pack heavy socks or slippers too, as no shoes are worn indoors. There is a full calendar of events, talks and retreats, so have a look at the programme. It is possible to stay with the monastic community for a time, but you must participate fully in the daily routine of meditation, meals and work.

Open: *March to December inclusive. Receives men, women, young people, sometimes families and groups, non-retreatants.*
Rooms: *Dormitories, but the sexes are separated.*

Facilities: *Park and library, pay phone.*
Spiritual Help: *Personal talks, formal and informal talks on the theory and practice of meditation and the spiritual life.*
Guests Admitted to: *Shrine room, work of the community, all daily routine.*
Meals: *Everyone eats together; rice-based Asian food.*
Special Activities: *Festivals, retreats, workshops. Send for brochure.*
Situation: *Quiet.*
Maximum Stay: *1 week, which can be extended at the discretion of the Guestmaster.*
Bookings: *By letter.*
Charges: *By donation and contributions to the cost of food.*
Access: *By car is easiest, but please drive slowly and carefully as the lanes to the Centre are narrow.*

St Albans

Verulam House
Verulam Road
St Albans
Herts. AL3 4DH   Telephone: 0727 53991

Anglican

Near St Albans Cathedral, this is a small Diocesan centre which is run for group retreats. Sometimes it is possible for individual retreatants to stay here, and various open events are being planned.

Open: *All year except August. Receives everyone.*
Rooms: *15 singles, 9 twin-bedded rooms.*
Facilities: *Conferences, garden, library, guest lounge and pay phone.*
Spiritual Help: *Personal talks.*
Guests Admitted to: *Unrestricted access to all areas, including chapel.*
Meals: *Everyone eats together. Varied food, with provision for vegetarian and special diets.*
Special Activities: *No planned programme of events.*
Situation: *Quiet, in the city, near St Albans Cathedral.*
Maximum Stay: *Not specified.*
Bookings: *By letter or telephone.*
Charges: *Various – please ask.*
Access: *By rail, bus or car to St Albans.*

Dereham

The Old Bakery
Hindolveston
Dereham
Norfolk NR20 5DF   Telephone: 0263 861325

Anglican – open to all

A modest programme of retreats is offered here in the private home
of the Reverend and Mrs Percy Gandon, and guests are welcomed as
part of the family. The Old Bakery is a restored 18th-century house,
with the added benefits of a games room, sun lounge and chapel. It is
a member of the Churches Council for Health and Healing and the
Association for Promoting Retreats.

Open: *All year. Receives men, women, young people, families,
groups and non-retreatants.*
Rooms: *4 singles, 5 doubles. Bring your own towels and bed linen.*
Facilities: *Conferences, chapel, garden, small library, guest lounge,
TV and pay phone.*
Spiritual Help: *Personal talks, group sharing, meditation, directed
study, healing ministry, counselling.*
Guests Admitted to: *Unrestricted access.*
Meals: *Everyone eats together. Traditional and wholefood, with
provision for vegetarian and special diets.*
Special Activities: *Planned programme of events including special
weekends. Send for brochure.*
Situation: *Quiet and in the village.*
Maximum Stay: *2 weeks.*
Bookings: *By letter or telephone.*
Charges: *£20 per day.*
Access: *BR: nearest main-line station (Norwich, King's Lynn) about
25 miles away. Bus: to Fakenham, 8 miles away, but guests can be
met. Car: via A148 – map available with booking confirmation.*

---

*'It is sad not to be loved,
but it is much sadder not to be able to love' – Miguel de Unamuno*

King's Lynn

Massingham St Mary
Little Massingham
Nr. King's Lynn
Norfolk PE32 2JU   Telephone: 0485 520245

Roman Catholic

Massingham St Mary is an informal and homely place, even if it is a
large country-house. The facilities are simple and basic but provide
all you probably need. Arrangements can be made for individually
directed retreats and for spiritual direction.

Open: *All year except Christmas, Easter and throughout September.*
Receives men, women, young people, families, groups. Non-retreat-
ants taken, if room available, for quiet time but not for a holiday.
Rooms: *22 singles, 8 doubles, plus a bungalow for 8 and a self-*
contained hermitage for 2–3. Bring soap and towels.
Facilities: *Limited for disabled, conferences, garden, library, guest*
lounge, TV and pay phone. Children welcomed.
Spiritual Help: *Personal talks, group sharing, meditation, directed*
study, spiritual direction and non-professional counselling.
Ignatian-trained guidance.
Guests Admitted to: *Unrestricted access to all areas, including*
chapels, choir.
Meals: *Everyone eats together in the guest house. Traditional food,*
with provision for vegetarian and special diets. Self-catering in the
bungalow and hermitage.
Special Activities: *Planned programme of events. Send for the*
brochure.
Situation: *Quiet, in the countryside.*
Maximum Stay: *According to length of programme event, or by*
personal arrangement.
Bookings: *By letter.*
Charges: *Programme fees in brochure. Retreats £25 per person per*
night - or what you can afford, if there is a problem.
Access: *By rail or car.*

'Our hearts are made for thee, O God,
and will not rest 'til they rest in thee' – St Augustine

Norwich

All Hallows House
Rouen Road
Norwich
Norfolk NR1 1QT   Telephone: 0603 624738

Anglican but open to all denominations

Though it is on a busy street, beset with traffic noise, All Hallows House has a peaceful atmosphere inside. St Julian's Church is next door and contains a chapel that is built on the site of the cell of the 14th-century mystic Julian of Norwich. Her *Revelations of Divine Love* is one of the classic English Christian works and can be obtained at most good bookshops.

Open: *All year. Receives men, women, small groups, families, and non-retreatants.*
Rooms: *2 singles, 2 doubles.*
Facilities: *Chapel, garden, small library, guest lounge, TV, guest telephone. Children welcome. No pets.*
Spiritual Help: *None.*
Guests Admitted to: *Chapel and fairly free access everywhere.*
Meals: *Everyone eats together for the evening meal. Traditional food. Vegetarian and special diets on request.*
Special Activities: *No special activities or events.*
Situation: *In the town, but despite the busy location, there seems to be a peace within.*
Maximum Stay: *14 days.*
Bookings: *Telephone in the first instance and confirm by letter.*
Charges: *By donation.*
Access: *By rail, bus or car to Norwich. Good map is available on request*

Norwich

Lavinia Cottage
40 The Close
Norwich
Norfolk   Telephone: 0603 614333

Christian

NORFOLK 117

Lavinia Cottage is a house in the Cathedral Close where two sisters from the Community of All Hallows live. They offer accommodation for two guests and vistors are welcome to stay for a few days.

Norwich

Bowthorpe Community Trust
1 St Michael's Cottages
Bowthorpe Hall Road
Bowthorpe
Norwich
Norfolk NR5 9AA   Telephone: 0603 746380

Interdenominational

The Trust offers short-stay accommodation set up through the combined sponsorship of Anglican, Baptist, Methodist, Quaker, Roman Catholic and United Reformed churches. Nearby is a woodcraft workshop for the disadvantaged. A small sitting room, a library and devotional books and a prayer and study room with all meals provided make this one of the more cosy places to stay. The Walsingham shrines are only an hour's drive away.

Open: *All year. Receives men, women and non-retreatants.*
Rooms: *1 single and 1 double.*
Facilities: *Garden, small library, private prayer and study rooms, TV.*
Spiritual Help: *Prayer cell and Worship Centre is available for private prayer and study.*
Guests Admitted to: *Most areas.*
Meals: *Everyone eats together. Traditional food with provision for vegetarians. No special diets.*
Special Activities: *No planned events but information brochure available.*
Situation: *Quiet, next to countryside.*
Maximum Stay: *3 weeks.*
Bookings: *By letter or telephone.*
Charges: *£46 per person per week, £9.20 per day.*
Access: *BR: from Norwich to Thorpe. Car: via A47.*

Norwich

Padmaloka Buddhist Retreat Centre for Men
Lesingham House
Surlingham
Norwich
Norfolk NR14 7AL   Telephone: 0508 538112

Buddhist

A Buddhist retreat centre for men only, run by the Western Buddhist
Order. Here, no time is wasted in getting you into stillness and
simplicity, and the study of what some claim to be the fastest growing spiritual tradition in the West. In addition to meditation and
other related classes, you can discover how to make spiritual practice
work in your career through talks by men who have achieved it.
They may be managing directors of successful companies or even
medical school lecturers – but all have developed what Buddhists
term 'Right Livehood'. Bring a sleeping-bag, towel, soap, and old
clothes and shoes for the work periods that everyone does during
the day. For meditation wear loose clothes. Vegetarians and vegans
can be catered for. A happy, peaceful and justly famous place.
Highly Recommended.

Open: *All year. Receives men only.*
Rooms: *Dormitories – bring your own towel and sleeping-bag.*
Facilities: *Disabled, garden, library, guest lounge and guest tele-
phone.*
Spiritual Help: *Personal talks, group sharing, meditation and
directed study.*
Guests Admitted to: *Unrestricted access. Shrineroom.*
Meals: *Everyone eats together. Vegetarian food. Vegan and special
diets catered for by prior arrangement.*
Special Activities: *Planned programme. Send for brochure.*
Situation: *Quiet, in a village and countryside.*
Maximum Stay: *Unlimited.*
Bookings: *By letter.*
Charges: *£22 per person per night. There are concessions, so please
enquire.*
Access: *By rail to Norwich then by taxi or bus. Bus to Surlingham
village drops you at the gate.*

Swaffham

Pickenham Resource Centre
Brecklands Green
North Pickenham
Swaffham
Norfolk PE37 8LG   Telephone: 0760 440427

Interdenominational

The Centre is part of the Pickenham Trust which also runs an activities camp and a book publishing enterprise. It is designed to cater for a great many people. Facilities range from a young people's camp to a piano and an organ, and even an outdoor relief map of the Holy Land. In many respects it is like a holiday place and, therefore, is perhaps best suited to the non-retreatant who wants a short break or to those who are attending the Centre as members of a group.

Open: *March to December. Receives men, women, young people, families, groups, non-retreatants.*
Rooms: *There are 67 beds, including singles, doubles, dormitories, plus an activities camp.*
Facilities: *Conferences, garden, bookshop, guest lounge, TV and pay phone. Children welcomed. Hoping soon to offer provision for the disabled, so please enquire.*
Spiritual Help: *See the programme on offer.*
Guests Admitted to: *Unrestricted access.*
Meals: *Everyone eats together. Traditional home-cooking, with provision for vegetarian and special diets. Self-catering possible at certain times of the year.*
Special Activities: *No planned programme of events.*
Situation: *Very quiet, in the countryside.*
Maximum Stay: *Unlimited.*
Bookings: *By letter or telephone.*
Charges: *Send for tariff.*
Access: *BR: to Downham Market, 11 miles away. Buses: to Swaffham from London, Norwich, King's Lynn, Peterborough.*

Walsingham

Shrine of Our Lady
The Accommodation Office
Little Walsingham
6 Common Place
Norfolk NR22 6BW   Telephone: 0328 820239

Anglican

Walsingham Shrine is a place of ancient Christian pilgrimage and is a famous pilgrimage centre. This means that you will not find facilities for silence or for spiritual guidance. To go on a pilgrimage to a holy place is a long-established religious practice of most major world faiths. It can, and ought to be, regarded as a kind of retreat, especially as the pilgrim hopes for a deepening of personal spirituality. Before starting out, read about the history of Walsingham so that you may understand what has drawn Christians there over the centuries. This should put meaning into what might otherwise simply be a visit to another 'monument'. The Centre is a pleasant place to stay and from which to visit either the local Anglican shrine or the Roman Catholic one a mile away. Both continue to attract thousands of people every year.

Open: *All year except mid-December to the end of January. Receives everyone.*
Rooms: *Over 200 places divided between single, double, and three-bedded accommodation.*
Facilities: *Disabled, conferences, garden, guest lounge, TV and pay phone. Children welcome.*
Spiritual Help: *No facilities for silence, and no on-site spiritual guidance.*
Guests Admitted to: *Unrestricted access.*
Meals: *Everyone eats together. Traditional food, with provision for vegetarians and special diets.*
Special Activities: *Each weekend there is a programme organised by the parish groups attending. This includes Stations of the Cross, Procession and Benediction.*
Situation: *Rather busy in the village, near countryside.*
Maximum Stay: *10 days, including only 1 weekend.*
Bookings: *By letter enclosing £6 deposit.*
Charges: *£24.32 per day.*
Access: *By car is best.*

Bungay

All Hallows House
Ditchingham
Bungay
Suffolk NR35 2DZ   Telephone: 0986-892749

Anglican

The Anglican Community of All Hallows run a number of establishments in addition to this All Hallow's House. There is Holy Cross
House with 15 rooms for those seeking to share in the worship of the
community. St. Mary's Lodge is a silent house for reflection and
prayer. St. Raphael's Centre is for self-catering and includes a games
room and swimming facilities while St. Gabriel's is for conferences.
If you think any of these houses more appropriate for you than All
Hallow's, then write and ask about them. See the next entry for details
of St. Michael's House.

Open: *All year except last week in August. Receives men, women,
families, small groups and non-retreatants.*
Rooms: *3 singles, 2 doubles, camping, hermitage, hostel.*
Facilities: *Chapel, large garden, guest lounge, TV and guest telephone. Children welcome. Pets sometimes but only by prior arrangement.*
Spiritual Help: *Individually guided retreats. The Chaplain, when
available, is willing to talk to visitors and occasionally to direct
personal retreats.*
Guests Admitted to: *Convent grounds, the garden and chapel.*
Meals: *Meals taken in guest house. Traditional and wholefood with
vegetarian meals and self-catering available. Tea and coffee facilities in every room.*
Special Activities: *Retreat programme - send for details.*
Situation: *Very quiet and in the countryside. The house is very
comfortable and homely, and guests are encouraged to help with
washing-up.*
Maximum Stay: *3 weeks.*
Bookings: *By letter or telephone.*
Charges: *By donation. £17.50 per person per day, full board is
suggested or £10 per day DIY.*
Access: *By car is best.*

Bungay

St Michael's House
All Hallows Convent
Ditchingham
Bungay
Suffolk NR35 2DT   Telephone: 0986 895749

Anglican

There is a peaceful, happy atmosphere here, and group retreatants often return on an individual basis. Open retreats of various kinds are held, bearing such titles as Beginners, Way of Life, Julian and Healing, while Advent and summer courses are available for residential groups of up to 25 people.

Open: *All year except Easter, Christmas and All Saints' Week. Receives men, women, young people, families, groups and non-retreatants.*
Rooms: *17 singles, 4 doubles.*
Facilities: *Conferences, chapel, garden, library, guest lounge, pay phone. Children welcome.*
Spiritual Help: *Personal talks, group sharing, meditation.*
Guests Admitted to: *Convent chapel and gardens.*
Meals: *Everyone eats in St Michael's House. Traditional food, with provision for vegetarian and special diets. The food is prepared by professional caterers.*
Special Activities: *Planned programme of events. Send for brochure.*
Situation: *Very quiet.*
Maximum Stay: *2 weeks.*
Bookings: *By telephone but confirm by letter.*
Charges: *By donation. £12.50 per person per day is suggested and £35 for a weekend.*
Access: *Car: via B1332 from Norwich to Bungay.*

Bury St Edmonds

Water Hall Retreat Centre
Great Ashfield
Bury St Edmonds
Suffolk IP31 3HP   Telephone: 081-981 1225
                                    for enquiries

Buddhist

Water Hall is run by the London Buddhist Centre specifically for introductory retreats. These are in the form of introductory weekend retreats for adults wishing to learn meditation as well as attending more advanced classes. Classes are taken by full-time practising Buddhists who are members of the Western Buddhist Order. There are also courses about Buddhism, where you can learn who the Buddha was, what he taught and what relevance his teaching has for us in the West today. The telephone number above is for the London Centre, who will deal with your enquiry.

Open: *During organised group retreats. Receives men, women, groups and religious only.*
Rooms: *Accommodation for 20 adults in double rooms, dormitories and a caravan.*
Facilities: *Disabled, conferences, camping, garden, guest lounge and pay phone.*
Spiritual Help: *Personal talks, group sharing, meditation and directed study.*
Guests Admitted to: *Unrestricted access everywhere, including shrine room and work of the community.*
Meals: *Everyone eats together. Vegetarian wholefood, with provision for special diets.*
Special Activities: *There is a special programme of planned events – see brochure. Water Hall is available (particularly during the week, from Monday to Friday) for use by groups sympathetic to Buddhism.*
Situation: *Very quiet, in the village and countryside. No passing traffic.*
Maximum Stay: *10 days.*
Bookings: *By letter or telephone.*
Charges: *See brochure as charges depend on course.*
Access: *By rail to Bury St Edmonds, or by car.*

Newmarket

The Old Stable House
3 Sussex Lodge
Fordham Road
Newmarket
Suffolk CB8 7AF   Telephone: 0638 667190

Roman Catholic – Inter-faith

Very close to Newmarket Heath with lots of good walks, this former stable offers a warm, comfortable environment with as much free-dom as possible for individuals and groups to work on their personal and spiritual development. The atmosphere is informal and home-like. The focus of the workshops is holistic and creation-centred to promote the integration of spiritual, physical, psychological and intellectual elements, and to help release the mysticism, creativity and wisdom inherent in each individual. Open to all who are committed to healing, growth and the desire to increase their spiritual awareness.

Open: *All year, except Christmas weeks. Receives men, women, groups, and non-retreatants.*
Rooms: *5 singles, 4 doubles.*
Facilities: *Disabled, conferences, camping, caravans (no facilities), park, garden, guest lounge and pay phone. Children welcomed. Pets permitted within reason.*
Spiritual Help: *Retreats and workshops designed to meet the needs of individual groups, in addition to group sharing, directed study, meditation, and counselling.*
Guests Admitted to: *Unrestricted access.*
Meals: *Self-catering for individual guests but it is hoped that these will be served in a guesthouse in the near future. Provision for vegetarians and special diets.*
Special Activities: *Planned programme of events. Send for bro-chure.*
Situation: *Quiet, with a small woodland area and paddock. 12 miles from Cambridge.*
Maximum Stay: *1 week, negotiable.*
Bookings: *By letter or telephone.*
Charges: *Send for leaflet – but charges are likely to range from £18 per day to £54 for a weekend.*
Access: *BR: Newmarket station 5 minutes away. Local buses. Car: via A45.*

'We can never know God
until we first know clearly our own soul' – Julian of Norwich

Central England

Ashram Community House
23–25 Grantham Road
Sparkbrook
Birmingham B11 1LU   Telephone: 021-773 7061

Christian – Non-denominational

This is a radical Christian community set in one of the poorest inner-city districts. It actively participates in a multi-cultural neighbourhood that is composed primarily of people from Pakistan. The community comprises some who live at the Ashram and many others who join on special projects which involve them in a wider community network. The Ashram works to foster relationships between Christians and Muslims. Most weekends see a number of guests in the house who want to find out more about this kind of Christian life which seeks to translate faith into radical action, responding to the challenge set by the gospel.

Open: *All year except 27 December to 2 January.*
Rooms: *More like impromptu sleeping arrangements than rooms, but all are singles.*
Facilities: *Chapel, lounge and reading material.*
Spiritual Help: *Group and personal talks.*
Guests Admitted to: *Everywhere except the business offices, and may participate in work projects of the community.*
Meals: *Everyone eats together. Provision for vegetarians.*
Special Activities: *There is a lot going on here, so you can probably join one or other of the current projects.*
Situation: *Busy, right in the middle of an urban area.*
Maximum Stay: *By arrangement.*
Bookings: *By letter, giving some details about yourself.*
Charges: *Depends on what you want to do at the Ashram, but no one is turned away simply because they have no money.*
Access: *BR or bus to Birmingham, then local bus. If you are arriving by car, ask about parking.*

Belper

Convent of St Lawrence
Field Lane
Belper
Derby DE5 1DD   Telephone: 0773 822585

Anglican

Open: *All year. Receives men, women, groups and non-retreatants.*
Rooms: *10 singles, 5 doubles.*
Facilities: *Conferences, guest lounge, TV and pay phone.*
Spiritual Help: *Personal talks if requested.*
Guests Admitted to: *Chapel.*
Meals: *Mostly taken together. Very plain food, with provision for vegetarians. DIY facilities.*
Special Activities: *No planned programme of events.*
Situation: *Very quiet, in a small town.*
Maximum Stay: *1 week.*
Bookings: *By telephone and confirm by letter.*
Charges: *Enquire when booking.*
Access: *BR: to Belper, then a 5-minute walk. Bus: from Derby to Belper. Car: via A6.*

Morley

Morley Retreat House
Church Lane
Morley, Ilkeston
Derby DE7 6DE   Telephone: 0332 831293

Anglican

Modern accommodation has been built for guests next to the old Morley Rectory. There is a good programme of retreat and house events, ranging from quiet days to a weekend devoted to silent prayer called, appropriately, 'Listening to God'. There is sometime a Taizé weekend to give you a taste of the spirituality and music of that popular and famous French community. While many of the retreat houses in this book say that they accept young people, what they usually mean is people who are in their 20s. At Morley teenagers will be welcomed to weekend retreats designed especially for them.

Open: *All year. Receives men, women, young people, families and groups.*

Rooms: *24 singles, 5 doubles. Bring soap and towels.*

Facilities: *Very limited for disabled, chapel, conferences, garden, 5 acre park, library, guest lounge, TV and pay phone. Children welcomed. Pets only by arrangement.*

Spiritual Help: *Depends on retreat programme so please enquire when booking.*

Guests Admitted to: *Unrestricted access.*

Meals: *Everyone eats together. Traditional food, with provision for vegetarian and special diets.*

Special Activities: *Planned programme of events. Send for brochure.*

Situation: *Very quiet, in the countryside, with a walled garden and 14th-century parish church, set in the midst of 5 acres of grounds.*

Maximum Stay: *By arrangement.*

Bookings: *By telephone or letter.*

Charges: *£23 per person for 24 hours.*

Access: *BR: to Derby, but there are no local bus services. Car: via M1, Exit 25, followed by A52, A61 and A608.*

GLOUCESTERSHIRE

Cranham

Prinknash Abbey
Cranham
Gloucester CL4 8EX   Telephone: 0452 812455

Roman Catholic

The monastery, built about twenty years ago, is very much an architectural design of that period, proudly sitting on its hill looking rather stark and modern - but inside all is warm, comfortable, and purpose-built. Men retreatants are received here in separate guest accommodation. Prinknash Abbey is a busy place with a number of commercial enterprises going on which help support the life and work of the community. This includes their famous pottery, some of which you can buy in the gift shop. The chapel is at the side of the monastery and gives the impression of going 'downstairs', but the liturgy is inspiring and there is a reassuring modesty in the simplicity of the place. You may attend the daily round of services and there is usually some work to do if you feel you want to contribute in that way. Do not telephone when booking as letters are preferred. There is a separate guesthouse open to all (see next entry).

Open: *Open all year except for Christmas Day and Boxing Day. Receives men only - over 18 years of age, groups of men up to seven in number at any one time, religious, and secular clergy.*
Rooms: *7 singles.*
Facilities: *Garden, park, library, guest lounge, pay phone.*
Guests Admitted to: *Unrestricted access except private community quarters, chapel.*
Spiritual Help: *All services in the church can be attended. This includes the Divine Office with daily Mass. Personal talks are available only if requested by a guest.*
Meals: *Everyone eats together. Traditional food. No provision for vegetarians but the meals contain plenty of vegetables. No special diets. DIY for tea and coffee.*
Special Activities: *None except the daily round of prayer and services.*
Situation: *On a great hill with sweeping views across the Cotswold countryside.*
Maximum Stay: *2 weeks.*
Bookings: *Letter only.*
Charges: *Not fixed – donations accepted.*
Access: *BR: Stroud from BR Paddington London or if coming from the North, then take train to Cheltenham. Bus: No.46 from Cheltenham or Stroud. Car: M5 then A46.*

Cranham

St. Peter's Grange
Cranham
Gloucester CL4 8EX   Telephone:
0452 813592

Roman Catholic

St Peter's Grange is the guest house of the monks of Prinknash Abbey (see above entry). It is a distinguished place of mainly Tudor buildings and was originally a monastic property connected with Gloucester Cathedral. It was used as the monastery by the present community of monks until they built a new Abbey in the 1970's. This is about a mile away but within the property and connected by a long drive. The Grange is a mellow pile of stone set against a hill with a small quiet garden entrance. Within, it is very comfortable with most of the panelling and other antique features retained. This includes a remarkably beautiful decorated chapel and choir.

Open: *All year except 20 December to 2 January. Receives men, women, young people, families, and groups (from Friday supper to Sunday lunch.)*
Rooms: *4 singles, 1 double, small dormitory rooms sleeping four each.*
Facilities: *Small conferences, garden, park, guest lounge, pay phone. There is a bird park and pottery. Children welcomed. Guide dogs only.*
Spiritual Help: *None.*
Guests Admitted to: *Chapel, Abbey church.*
Meals: *Everyone eats together. Basic traditional food. Provision for vegetarians. Special diets only if guests bring their own food.*
Special Activities: *None.*
Situation: *Very quiet in the countryside.*
Maximum Stay: *Monday to Friday.*
Bookings: *By letter.*
Charges: *By donation but £15 per day full board is suggested.*
Access: *BR: Stroud from BR Paddington London or if coming from the North, then take train to Cheltenham. Bus: No.46 from Cheltenham or Stroud. Car: M5 then A46.*

Stroud

More Hall Convent
Randwick
Stroud
Glos. GL6 6EP   Telephone: 0453 764486

Roman Catholic

Open: *All year. Receives men, women, young people, families and non-retreatants.*
Rooms: *3 bed-sitting rooms, hermitage.*
Facilities: *Garden, library, guest lounge TV, pay phone. Children welcome.*
Spiritual Help: *Personal talks, directed study, Divine Office.*
Guests Admitted to: *Chapel and sometimes the work of the community which is care of the elderly.*

Meals: *Everyone eats together. Traditional food, with provision for vegetarians. DIY facilities.*
Special Activities: *No special activities.*
Situation: *Quiet and in the countryside.*
Maximum Stay: *Usually 2 weeks.*
Bookings: *By letter.*
Charges: *No fixed charge.*
Access: *BR: to Stroud then by bus. Enquire for car-route directions at time of booking.*

HEREFORD and WORCESTER

Hereford

Belmont Abbey
Hereford HR2 9RZ   Telephone: 0432 277475

Roman Catholic

The community at Belmont Abbey has forged ahead in offering increased guest facilities and a full programme of courses as well as more and better accommodation. Many visitors come specifically for the choral monastic offices. The monks serve as well out in the surrounding countryside so many of the guests may be local people. The school attached to the Abbey is justly famous. This is probably one of the very few monastic communities whose hospitality extends to providing TV in guest rooms.

Open: *All year. Receives men, women, young people, families, groups and non-retreatants.*
Rooms: *9 singles, 9 doubles, dormitories available in school holidays.*
Facilities: *Conferences, camping, park, library,TV, pay phone. Disabled people and children considered.*
Spiritual Help: *Personal talks, group sharing, meditation, and counselling.*
Guests Admitted to: *Chapel; only clergy permitted in choir, only male retreatants admitted to monastic enclosure.*
Meals: *Eaten in guest house. Men only in refectory.Traditional food with provision for vegetarians.*
Special Activities: *Planned programme of events. Send for the brochure.*
Situation: *Quiet, and in the countryside but incorporating an active*

boys' school. Close to beautiful countryside, River Wye, Welsh mountains, golf course and school sports facilities.
Maximum Stay: *9 days.*
Bookings: *By letter.*
Charges: *Single B&B £12 or Ensuite B&B £18.50.*
Access: *Hereford is easily reached by rail, bus or car.*

Hereford

Vipassana Trust
Dhamma Dipa
Harewood End
Hereford HR2 8NG   Telephone: 098 987234

Non-sectarian

Vipassana means 'to see things as they really are'. It is a way of self-purification by self-observation and is one of India's most ancient meditation techniques. The Trust offers a 10-day course in it as taught by S.N. Goenka, to which you must give all your efforts, observing the rules of the house and taking your study seriously. There are also courses available for Punjabi and Hindi speakers. People come here to meditate, serve on courses or to help with improvement of the property which is set in 22 acres of gentle rolling countryside near the cathedral city of Hereford. There are local practising Vipassana groups in London, Bedfordshire, Bristol, Liverpool, Suffolk, Sussex, Devon and Wales.

Open: *All year. Receives men, women and young people for specific short courses and for childrens' days.*
Rooms: *Single accommodation available on small courses, otherwise 20 doubles, 8 plus domitories, space for camping. At present up to 70 students can be accommodated. Men and women are segregated.*
Facilities: *Basic.*
Spiritual Help: *Meditation and directed study.*
Guests Admitted to: *Almost everywhere, but male and female guests have designated and separate areas.*
Meals: *The food is vegetarian but sufficient. Men and women eat separately.*
Special Activities: *Send for information.*
Situation: *Quiet in the countryside.*
Maximum Stay: *10 days initially. Afterwards by arrangement.*

Bookings: *By letter.*
Charges: *By donation at the end of course*
Access: *Sent with booking information.*

Pershore

Holland House
Retreat and Conference Centre
Cropthorne
Pershore
Worcs. WR10 3NB   Telephone: 0386 860330

Interdenominational

Holland House was set up to help people who are trying to relate their prayer life more closely to the world around them. It is a big old 17th-century place, with lots of thatch and gardens laid out by Lutyens. There is a new chapel and a modern conference and bedroom wing. The house is close to the village church, and although not far from busy roads, it is quiet.

Open: *All year except Christmas and the week after Easter. Receives men, women, young people, families, groups and non-retreatants.*
Rooms: *18 singles, 6 doubles.*
Facilities: *Conferences, garden, library, guest lounge and pay phone. Children welcome.*
Spiritual Help: *All possible help is given to guests to make best use of their stay. A variety of retreats, courses and quiet days are on offer.*
Guests Admitted to: *Almost unrestricted access.*
Meals: *Homestyle food with provision for vegetarians and special diets.*
Special Activities: *Planned programme of events. Send for the brochure.*
Situation: *Quiet, in the village and countryside.*
Maximum Stay: *Unlimited.*
Bookings: *By letter, but telephone about course availability.*
Charges: *Send for details.*
Access: *BR: to Evesham, $3^1/_2$ miles away. Buses: from Evesham. Car: via M5, Exit 7, then A44.*

Shrawley

Society of St Francis
Glasshampton Monastery
Shrawley
Worcs. WR6 6TQ   Telephone: 0299 896345

Anglican

Open: *All year except for 1 week in August. Receives men.*
Rooms: *5 singles.*
Facilities: *Garden, library, guest lounge, guest telephone.*
Spiritual Help: *Personal talks, taking part in the worship of the brothers. There are 4 offices a day and a daily Eucharist.*
Guests Admitted to: *Chapel.*
Meals: *Everyone eats together. Wholefood with provision for vegetarians.*
Special Activities: *No planned programme of events.*
Situation: *Quiet and peaceful, in the countryside.*
Maximum Stay: *1 week.*
Bookings: *By letter.*
Charges: *£10 per person per day.*
Access: *By bus or car (not rail).*

Worcester

St Mary's House
Stanbrook Abbey
Callow End
Worcester
Worcs. WR2 4TD   Telephone: 0905 830307

Roman Catholic

St Mary's is the guest house of Stanbrook Abbey, one of the best-known Benedictine communities in Britain, with a national reputation for literary, musical and artistic work. Its influence can be seen and heard in the liturgical arrangements of many other monastic communities. This is a classic Christian place for making a private retreat.

Open: *All year except 2 weeks at Christmas and during annual community retreat. Receives men, women, young people and a*

restricted number of groups.
Rooms: *10 singles, 4 doubles.*
Facilities: *Disabled, conferences, guest-house chapel, garden, library, guest lounge and pay phone.*
Spiritual Help: *Guests are welcome to attend Divine Office in the church.*
Guests Admitted to: *Extern chapel and guesthouse facilities.*
Meals: *Eaten in the guest house. Traditional food, with provision for vegetarian and special diets. DIY for breakfast.*
Special Activities: *No planned programme of events, but send for brochure describing the facilities.*
Situation: *Quiet and in the village.*
Maximum Stay: *2 weeks.*
Bookings: *Preferably by letter.*
Charges: *£20 per person per night. £18 per person for two or more nights.*
Access: *BR: to Worcester Shrub Hill or Foregate Street, then by taxi. Buses are very infrequent. Car: via M5, Exit 8, then take Malvern Road.*

LEICESTERSHIRE

Coalville

Mount St Bernard Abbey
Coalville
Leics. LE6 3UL   Telephone: 0530 832298

Roman Catholic

Built of local stone, the buildings are simple, not over-ornate, and in keeping with the Cistercian traditions. In the fine and very large granite church, Latin Mass is sung once a month and the vernacular Mass daily. Rooms are clean, comfortable, look out on to a courtyard, and have good new beds. Although the rooms are heated, pyjamas are a good idea. There is a small library of general spiritual texts in the main corridor of the guest house, with more specific texts for study available from the Chapter House. The Abbey has a large working pottery, as well as carpentry and printing shops. Meals are very traditional and contain lots of vegetables as these are raised by the monks. Located in the middle of the famous Quorn Hunt country, the Abbey offers good walking over hill, pasture and moor. But be warned

that this monastery is a very popular place and you may find it hard
to get accommodation except by booking well in advance.

Open: *All year except February and over the Christmas period.
Receives men, women, young people, families sometimes, groups,
retreatants.*
Rooms: *Singles and doubles available in main guesthouse and in a
guesthouse specially for women.*
Facilities: *Garden, park, library, guest lounge and telephone. Chil-
dren only permitted by prior arrangement.*
Spiritual Help: *Personal talks if required.*
Guests Admitted to: *Chapel, choir, sometimes the work of the
community, but not monastic enclosure.*
Meals: *Taken in guesthouse. Traditional, plain food with provision
for vegetarians if required.*
Special Activities: *No planned programme.*
Situation: *150-acre estate in hills of Charnwood Forest, with com-
manding views of Soar river-valley.*
Maximum Stay: *By arrangement.*
Bookings: *By letter.*
Charges: *By donation.*
Access: *BR: to Loughborough, then by taxi. Car: via M1, Exit 23.*

East Norton

Launde Abbey
East Norton
Leics. LE7 9XB   Telephone: 057286 254

Anglican

This is a huge red-brick house built by Thomas Cromwell in 1540 on
the site of an early Augustinian priory. It retains today the comfort and
charm of a distinguished private country-mansion, with a cheerful
drawing room fire, a panelled dining-room and games room. A
beautiful chapel, still intact from the 15th century, is the jewel of
Launde Abbey. You might be given a room in either the house, a small
annexe or in the refurbished Georgian stable-block, which overlooks
a large pond.

Open: *All year except August and week after Christmas. Receives
men, women, young people, families, groups and non-retreatants.*
Rooms: *15 singles, 21 doubles, a hermitage.*

Facilities: *Disabled, conferences, chapel, garden, park, library, guest lounge, TV and pay phone. Children welcomed.*
Spiritual Help: *Personal talks. Three spiritual directors are available and a qualified psychotherapist.*
Guests Admitted to: *Almost everywhere.*
Meals: *Everyone eats together. Traditional food, with provision for vegetarian and special diets.*
Special Activities: *Planned programme of events. Send for the brochure.*
Situation: *Very quiet, in the countryside.*
Maximum Stay: *Usually six days.*
Bookings: *By letter or telephone.*
Charges: *£25 per person per 24 hours.*
Access: *BR: to Oakham, 6 miles away. Bus: No. 147 to Leicester. Car: via A47 from Leicester.*

Theddingworth

Hothorpe Hall
Theddingworth
Leics. LE17 6QX   Telephone: 0858 880257

Interdenominational

Hothorpe Hall is a conference centre where Christian organisations arrange their own programme and bring their own speakers. Much effort has gone into improving the comfort of the rooms and many boast en-suite facilities. There is also a new 200-seat conference room. The garden runs to 12 acres, so there is plenty of space and quiet.

Open: *All year. Receives groups.*
Rooms: *45 rooms comprising some singles but mainly double.*
Facilities: *Disabled, conferences, recreation, chapel, garden, park, library, guest lounge, TV and pay phone.*
Spiritual help: *None.*
Guests Admitted to: *Unrestricted access to all areas, including some parts of the Hall.*
Meals: *Everyone eats together. Traditional food.*
Special Activities: *See above description.*
Situation: *Very quiet, close to the village and in the countryside.*
Maximum Stay: *By the length of the group activity which has been arranged.*

Bookings: *By letter or telephone.*
Charges: *Send for details.*
Access: *to Market Harborough, 5 miles away.*

NORTHAMPTONSHIRE

Ecton

Peterborough Diocesan Retreat House
Ecton House
Church Way
Ecton
Northants NN6 OQE   Telephone: 0604 406442

Anglican

This is a late-17th-century rectory set in a charming village between
Northampton and Wellingborough. It is a warm, comfortable place
with a family atmosphere.

Open: *All year except 2 weeks at Christmas, 2 weeks at Easter and
some of August. Receives men, women, young people, groups and
non-retreatants.*
Rooms: *26 singles, 1 double.*
Facilities: *Conferences, chapel, garden, library, guest lounge, TV
and pay phone. Children welcomed.*
Spiritual Help: *Personal talks, group sharing, meditation, directed
study.*
Guests Admitted to: *Unrestricted access to all areas, including
chapel.*
Meals: *Everyone eats together. Traditional food, with provision for
vegetarian and special diets.*
Special Activities: *Planned programme of events. Send for bro-
chure.*
Situation: *Quiet, in the village and countryside.*
Maximum Stay: *Unlimited.*
Bookings: *By letter or telephone.*
Charges: *Send for price list.*
Access: *BR: to Northampton. Local buses: Nos. 45, 46. Car: to
Northampton near M1 Exit 15.*

Burford

**Priory of Our Lady
Burford
Oxon. OX8 4SQ**

Telephone: 0993 823605

Anglican

Pretty Burford, with its stone houses, antique shops, tourists and air of new money and material success, is also the home of a community of Benedictine monks and nuns. The guesthouse is a late 16th century house in its own gardens within the Priory grounds. The bedrooms are well-equipped and, in addition to guest kitchen and sittingroom, there is an oratory. Disabled people who are semi-ambulant have the benefit of that rare monastic facility – an electric lift to the first-floor accommodation, which includes a bathroom for the disabled. **Highly Recommended.**

Open: *All year except Christmas and Easter. Receives men, women, young people, families, groups and non-retreatants if visiting for rest and study.*
Rooms: *2 singles, 6 doubles plus additonal accommodation.*
Facilities: *Some for the disabled, small conferences, chapel, gardens, park, library, guest lounge and pay phone. Children welcome in the retreat house.*
Spiritual Help: *Personal talks, directed study, individually guided retreats, non-resident groups.*
Guests Admitted to: *Chapel, choir and some work of the community.*
Meals: *Everyone eats together or in the guest house, depending on numbers. Traditional food, with provision for vegetarians and special diets. DIY facilities.*
Special Activities: *Enquire about events. There are Benedictine Experience Weeks and individually guided retreats.*
Situation: *Quiet, in the village – splendid views of Windrush Valley.*
Maximum Stay: *1 week.*
Bookings: *By letter with deposit.*
Charges: *By donation. Guideline is £19 per day or £7 per pastoral session.*
Access: *BR: Charlebury station is 8 miles away. Or travel to Oxford and take a bus. Buses: from Oxford/Cheltenham.*

Charney Bassett

Charney Manor
Charney Bassett
nr. Wantage
Oxon. OX12 OEJ   Telephone: 0235 868206

Religious Society of Friends (Quakers)

The Manor is a Grade 1 listed house. There are just two Friends living here, so there is not really a resident community as such, but a warm welcome awaits all guests none the less. Quaker workshop meetings are held every Wednesday evening.

Open: *All year. Receives men, women, young people, families, groups and non-retreatants.*
Rooms: *Main house for group bookings only – 10 singles, 10 twin-bedded rooms in addition to folding beds. Self-catering cottage; barn can be used for overflow, with camping-style accommodation.*
Facilities: *Conferences, garden, library, guest lounge, TV, guest telephone and pay phone. Children welcomed.*
Spiritual Help: *Depending on nature of group's programme at any time.*
Guests Admitted to: *Unrestricted access everywhere.*
Meals: *Everyone eats together. Traditional and wholefood –vegetarian and special diets can be catered for with advance notice.*
Special Activities: *Planned programme of retreats. Send for brochure.*
Situation: *Very quiet, in the countryside, on edge of village. Nearest shop $3^1/_2$ miles.*
Maximum Stay: *Negotiable but usually a weekend.*
Bookings: *By telephone or letter.*
Charges: *See brochure - about £59 for the weekend.*
Access: *BR: to Didcot station, 11 miles away, then by taxi. Bus: runs from Southmoor, 3 miles away.*

Faringdon

St Mary's Priory
Fernham
Faringdon
Oxon. SN7 7PP   Telephone: 0367 240133

Roman Catholic

The guesthouse, St. Gabriel's, is a new Scandinavian chalet in the grounds. Set in the Vale of the White Horse with good views.

Open: *All year except first fortnight of August. Receives men, women, young people, and groups.*
Rooms: *4 doubles.*
Facilities: *Garden, guest lounge.*
Spiritual Help: *Personal talks if requested.*
Guests Admitted to: *Chapel.*
Meals: *Taken in the guesthouse - DIY with food provided. Self-catering available.*
Special Activities: *Participation in daily Mass and the Divine Office.*
Situation: *Very quiet, in the Vale of the White Horse, with unbroken views over Downs. Nearest shops 3 miles away.*
Maximum Stay: *10 days.*
Bookings: *By letter.*
Charges: *By donation.*
Access: *BR: to Oxford or Swindon. Bus: No. 66 from Oxford/ Swindon. Car: via A420 – take turning signposted to Fernham and White Horse Hill.*

Nuneham Courtney

Global Retreat Centre
Brahma Kumaris World Spirituality University
Nuneham Park, Nuneham Courtney
Oxon OX44 9PG   Telephone: 086 738551

Non-religious

In the summer of 1993, the Brahma Kumaris World Spiritual University (see entry in London) opened this Centre in a magnificent Palladian Villa built by the Earl of Harcourt in 1756. George II called it, 'The most enjoyable place I know.'and Queen Victoria wrote after her visit, 'This is a most lovely place, with pleasure grounds in the style of Claremont'. About 15 minutes drive from Oxford, the house is situated by the River Thames in 60 acres of land and gardens.The Centre is staffed by teachers of meditation who are experienced in creating an atmosphere of peace and spirituality. As well as regular retreats lasting from one day to one week, a variety of seminars, workshops, and courses offer a range of opportunities to learn meditation, develop personal skills, and explore the common values essential to world harmony.The Global Retreat Centre is not operated like the usual retreat guest house where you book and stay. Here, a series of events is organised including retreats throughout the year to which people are invited.

Open: *All year. Receives men, women, young people, families, groups and non-retreatants. The building is open to the public during certain weekends of the year.*
Rooms: *Some single but mainly double rooms.*
Facilities: *Conferences, garden, park, guest lounge and guest telephone.*
Spiritual Help: *Personal talks, group sharing, meditation, directed study.*
Guests Admitted to: *Unrestricted access.*
Meals: *Only vegetarian food is served, some Western and some Indian cuisine. No alcohol is allowed.*
Special Activities: *Planned programme of events. Ask for information.*
Situation: *Very quiet in its own parkland surrounded by countryside.*
Maximum Stay: *2 weeks per year.*
Bookings: *By letter, or telephone between 6.00 and 7.00 p.m. only.*
Charges: *Voluntary contribution.*
Access: *BR: to Oxford. Car: M40 or from Oxford.*

Oxford

Carmelite Priory
Boars Hill
Oxford OX1 5HB   Telephone: 0865 730183

Roman Catholic

Boars Hill is an ideal location for this centre run by the Teresian Discalced Carmel Friars. The Centre, where a lot of new building has been done to offer even better facilities, stands in its own 17 acres of woodland. It aims to provide courses on prayer and spirituality, special attention being given to the teaching on prayer of the great Carmelite writers, such as St Teresa of Avila, St John of the Cross and St Teresa of Lisieux. Sometimes arrangements can be made for individuals who desire to experience a hermitage retreat. This will be discussed with you – but it is unlikely that a person with a busy lifestyle, going on a retreat for the first time, is really a suitable candidate for such a period of silent contemplation. There is an annual 'vocation' weekend open to all young men interested in the religious

OXFORDSHIRE 143

life and the Carmelites in particular. The programme of planned retreats and events is an exciting, intelligent and full one. **Highly Recommended.**

Open: *All year except Christmas and New Year. Receives men, women, young people, families and groups.*
Rooms: *12 singles, 17 doubles.*
Facilities: *Disabled, chapel, conferences, garden, park, guest lounge with pay phone, book service.*
Spiritual Help: *In addition to the round of religious services, there are planned retreats.*
Guests Admitted to: *Unrestricted access except to private community quarters.*
Meals: *Everyone eats together. DIY facilities available. Traditional food with provision for vegetarian and special diets when possible.*
Special Activities: *There is an exciting and full programme of retreats and events. Send for brochure.*
Situation: *Very quiet, in the countryside.*
Maximum Stay: *1 week.*
Bookings: *By telephone but confirm by letter with a deposit.*
Charges: *£20 per day suggested.*
Access: *BR: to Oxford (5 miles away), then by taxi. Car: via A34 – send for a map as route is a little complicated.*

Oxford

The Cherwell Centre
14-16 Norman Gardens
Oxford OX2 6QB   Telephone: 0865 52106

Roman Catholic

A new team of religious sisters has taken charge here. They plan to develop a retreat and workshop programme.

Open: *All year except August and over Christmas and Easter. Receives men, women, young people, groups and non-retreatants.*
Rooms: *22 singles, 9 doubles.*
Facilities: *Conferences, garden, nearby park, library, guest lounge, TV and pay phone.*
Spiritual Help: *Personal talks, spiritual direction and individually guided retreats. Many different groups use the residential and non-residential conference and retreat facilities.*

Guests Admitted to: *Chapel.*
Meals: *Everyone ea:s together. Good variety of food, with provison for vegetarian and special diets.*
Special Activities: *No special programme.*
Situation: *In the city – quiet, but rather busy during conferences.*
Maximum stay: *2 weeks*
Bookings: *By letter or telephone.*
Charges: *On request.*
Access: *BR: to Oxford. Buses: enquire at Oxford bus station. Car: any route to Oxford.*

Sutton Courtenay

The Abbey Community
The Abbey
Sutton Courtenay
nr. Abingdon
Oxon. OX14 4AF

Telephone: 0235 847401

Inter-faith

The aim of this small community of men and women is to discover the universal truth of Christ within the particular issues of our own day. The Abbey has been going for a number of years and the community is engaged in projects ranging from the dynamics of unemployment to the complementary relationship of men and women working in the ministry. The programme of events is designed to encourage personal, social and ecological transformation. There are many courses on offer at the Abbey, including Radical Christianity and the Green Movement, Tibetan healing exercises, the study of inner sound, non-violence and the social order, Buddhists and Christians in social action, art and consciousness, spirituality and ecology, intuitive massage, and Shiatsu.

Open: *All visits by arrangement. Receives men, women, young people, groups – especially midweek. Gandhians welcomed.*
Rooms: *4 singles, 5 doubles, dormitories and camping for organised groups.*
Facilities: *Limited for disabled, conferences, camping, park, library with Gandhi archive, craft centre, dining room, pay phone. No pets.*
Spiritual Help: *Personal talks, meditation, planned retreats and study breaks.*
Guests Admitted to: *restricted access, work of the community.*

Meals: *Wholefood, vegetarian and special diets by arrangement. Self-catering facilities.*
Special Activities: *Courses on crafts and sculpture. Green lectures. Gandhi school of non-violence programme has been offered most years.*
Situation: *Surrounded by 4 acres of wooded grounds, the Abbey is archaeologically important because of the underlying Roman and Saxon remains. Location is quiet, in a village.*
Maximum Stay: *By arrangement.*
Bookings: *By letter.*
Charges: *On application as charges may vary.*
Access: *BR: to Didcot Parkway, 3 miles away. Bus: No. 32 from Oxford runs every half hour. Car: via A34.*

SHROPSHIRE

Ellesmere

The Grange
Ellesmere
Shropshire SY12 9DE   Telephone: 0691 623495

Christian - Interfaith

Rooted in Christianity but open to all faiths, the Grange offers both traditional meditation study and a New Age approach, reflected in a range of courses from yoga and stress management to sacred dance. For older women there is a weekend to reflect, reassess and search for new personal potential within the security of a small group. Those who delight in nature may find on offer a course on how to link their concern for the environment with a life of prayer. The main interest here is in exploring womens' spirituality, especially in the second half of life.

Open: *March to October inclusive. Receives men, women, young people, families, groups, and non-retreatants.*
Rooms: *5 singles, 11 doubles. Most rooms have en-suite and tea/coffee-making facilities.*
Facilities: *Disabled, conferences, meditation area, garden, pasture and woodland, small library, guest lounge, TV, guest telephone.*
Spiritual Help: *Personal talks, meditation, yoga tuition, reflex therapy.*
Guests Admitted to: *Reasonably unrestricted access.*

Meals: *Everyone eats together. Wholefood (mainly vegetarian), with provision for special diets.*
Special Activities: *The aim of the courses is to promote international understanding and to explore the potential of women for healing and peace-making, especially in the second half of life.*
Situation: *Quiet, near a small town.*
Maximum Stay: *5 days.*
Bookings: *By letter or telephone.*
Charges: *£24 to £27.50 per day. Bed and board may be earned by 4–5 hours of gardening work each day .*
Access: *BR: to Shrewsbury, 17 miles away. Infrequent buses. Car: via A528 from Ellesmere.*

Shrewsbury

Hawkstone Hall
Weston-under-Redcastle
Shrewsbury
Shropshire SY4 5LG   Telephone: 063 084 242

Roman Catholic - Interdenominational

Hawkstone Hall is a great pile of a country-house, whose rooms contain fine plasterwork and much decoration. There is a comfortable modern wing more suited to the scale of a personal retreat; but no less than five guest lounges should give you an idea of what to expect. If you are disabled, then forget it as there are stairs and more stairs. This is basically a centre for men and women who have been in the service of the Church for a long time and need a period of renewal, but groups are welcomed at other times.

Open: *All year, except August. Receives groups and non-retreatants. Groups are received when no courses are in progress.*
Rooms: *64 singles, 1 double.*
Facilities: *Conferences, chapel, garden, park, library, guest lounges, TV and pay phone.*
Spiritual Help: *None.*
Guests Admitted to: *Reasonably unrestricted to all areas, including chapel, but not to the community area.*
Meals: *Everyone eats together. Traditional food, with provision for vegetarian and special diets.*
Special Activities: *Courses only.*
Situation: *Very quiet, in the countryside.*

Maximum Stay: *By arrangement.*
Bookings: *By letter.*
Charges: *£27.50 per day.*
Access: *There are no buses and BR stations are distant. Transport can be arranged on request, so do enquire. Car: via A41 from Whitchurch turning on to the A442.*

Whitchurch

Taraloka Buddhist Retreat Centre for Women
Cornhill Farm
Bettisfield
nr. Whitchurch
Shropshire SY12 2LV   Telephone: 094875 646

Buddhist

Situated peacefully on the plains of the Welsh borderlands, this Buddhist women's community has been going for over five years and acts as a focal point for women throughout the world from various walks of life. It provides inspiration, relaxation and affords a glimpse of new spiritual and personal vistas for all who come. The retreat centre is separate from the community house, but many of the facilities are shared, as well as meals. Workshops include meditation, music and movement, yoga, and special retreats for newcomers. Teachers are well qualified both in Buddhist teaching and in their specialist subject, such as music. Other features are yoga weekends, spiritual life and motherhood, and retreats designed for older women. A place of peace and self discovery. **Highly Recommended.**

Open: *Specific programme of retreats for women – no other guests received.*
Rooms: *Dormitories, each sleeping 22 women.*
Facilities: *Guest lounge, caravans accommodating 2–3, camping site.*
Spiritual Help: *Meditation and study. The programme teaches Buddhist meditation and study within the context of the Friends of the Western Buddhist order. Introductory events are also offered in addition to those only open to the more experienced.*
Guests Admitted to: *Shrine room.*
Meals: *Everyone eats together; all meals are vegetarian or vegan. Special diets catered for.*

Special Activities: *Planned events – see brochure.*
Situation: *Very quiet, in the countryside with beautiful country walks – near the Shropshire Union Canal. Nearby is a peat moss of special scientific interest.*
Maximum Stay: *10 days.*
Bookings: *By letter.*
Charges: *According to length of stay.*
Access: *Map and details are provided with booking confirmation.*

STAFFORDSHIRE

Stone

Shallowford House
Lichfield Diocesan Retreat & Conference Centre
Norton Bridge, Stone
Staffs. ST16 ONZ　　　　　　　　Telephone: 0785 760233

Anglican

Open: *All year, except August and over Easter and Christmas. Receives men, women, and groups.*
Rooms: *15 singles, 12 doubles.*
Facilities: *Disabled, conferences, chapel, large garden, library, guest lounge, TV and pay phone.*
Spiritual Help: *Counselling available.*
Guests Admitted to: *Chapel.*
Meals: *Everyone eats together. Traditional cooking, with provision for vegetarian and special diets if advance warning given.*
Special Activities: *Planned programme of events. Send for brochure.*
Situation: *Quiet and in the countryside.*
Maximum Stay: *4 nights.*
Bookings: *By letter or telephone.*
Charges: *Available on application. Weekend programmes range from £51 to £62.*
Access: *BR: to Norton Bridge. No buses.*

'Compassion is aroused when we realise we are One with all life'
– Throssel Hole Buddhist Priory

Leamington Spa

Offa House
Offchurch
Leamington Spa
War. CV33 9AS   Telephone: 0926 423309

Anglican

The Coventry Diocesan Retreat House and Conference Centre is situated in an old Georgian vicarage, with a large garden. The house has been organised in such a way that all visitors are helped to feel that this is their own 'special' place, and the staff try to be non-intrusive.

Open: *All year. Receives men, women, young people, families, groups and non-retreatants.*
Rooms: *16 singles, 8 doubles.*
Facilities: *Disabled, conferences, chapel, garden, library, bookstall, guest lounge, TV and pay phone. Children welcomed.*
Spiritual Help: *Personal talks and the opportunity to join in events offered by other groups.*
Guests Admitted to: *Chapel.*
Meals: *Everyone eats together. Meals are traditional, with a bias towards wholefood and provision for vegetarian and special diets.*
Special Activities: *Planned programme of events. Send for brochure.*
Situation: *Quiet, in the village and countryside.*
Maximum Stay: *Unlimited.*
Bookings: *By letter or telephone.*
Charges: *£6 per person per night for guests applying individually.*
Access: *Rail, bus, car and airport links are all excellent.*

Solihull

Monastery of Poor Clares
Rising Lane
Knowle
Solihull
War. B93 0DE

Roman Catholic

Simple but comfortable accommodation in a lovely part of Warwickshire close to Baddesley Clinton Manor, a National Trust property. Nice countryside walks all around.

Open: *All year – all are welcome.*
Rooms: *Converted brewhouse with double bunk beds.*
Facilities: *Camping, garden and guest lounge.*
Spiritual Help: *Some personal talks can be arranged.*
Guests Admitted to: *Chapel, sharing in the Divine Office - seating for guests outside enclosed area.*
Meals: *Self-catering only.*
Special Activities: *No planned programme, but there is an atmosphere of peace and simplicity.*
Situation: *Very quiet.*
Maximum Stay: *1 week.*
Bookings: *By letter.*
Charges: *A donation to cover basic costs would be appreciated.*
Access: *Enquire when you write.*

'To rejoice at another person's joy is like being in heaven'
– Meister Eckhart

Northern England

Chester

Chester Diocesan Retreat House
11 Abbey Square
Chester
Cheshire CH1 2HU   Telephone: 0244 321801

Anglican

The sisters lead retreats and quiet days when asked. In addition there are individually guided retreats and Myers-Briggs workshops.

Open: *All year except August. Receives men, women, groups and non-retreatants.*
Rooms: *29 singles, 3 doubles.*
Facilities: *Conferences, chapel, garden, library, guest lounge and telephone.*
Spiritual Help: *Personal talks, group sharing, meditation, group sharing, guided retreats, and directed study as required.*
Guests Admitted to: *Unrestricted access except to the sisters' quarters.*
Meals: *Everyone eats together. Traditional food – vegetarians are catered for and there is limited provision for special diets by arrangement only.*
Special Activities: *Planned programme of events. Send for brochure.*
Situation: *In the city square, by the cathedral.*
Maximum Stay: *1 week.*
Bookings: *By telephone but confirm by letter.*
Charges: *£20 per person per 24 hours.*
Access: *By rail, bus or car to Chester.*

Crewe

Oblate Retreat Centre
Wistaston Hall
89 Broughton Lane
Crewe
Cheshire CW2 8JS   Telephone: 0270 68653

Roman Catholic – Ecumenical

This is a 200-year old country-house, set in six acres of garden and peaceful countryside. The Centre is staffed by two Oblate Fathers and up to 41 guests can be accommodated. The aim is to enable those who come here to wind down from the stresses and strains of modern living and to enter into a deeper experience of prayer and reflection in the presence of Christ. Much effort goes into making guests feel comfortable with professional catering for meals and log fires in the winter months. **Highly Recommended.**

Open: *All year except August. Receives men, women, young people, families, groups, religious, and non-retreatants.*
Rooms: *1 single, 19 doubles, some ensuite.*
Facilities: *Disabled – some ground-floor rooms, conferences, chapel, large garden, library, guest lounge, TV and pay phone. Children welcomed.*
Spiritual Help: *Personal talks, group sharing, meditation, directed study.*
Guests Admitted to: *Unrestricted access to all areas, including chapel.*
Meals: *Everyone eats together. Traditional wholefood with provision for vegetarian and special diets, cooked by a professional chef.*
Special Activities: *Planned programme of events, including preached retreats with one over Holy Week. Send for brochure.*
Situation: *Very quiet, in the village and countryside.*
Maximum Stay: *By arrangement.*
Bookings: *By letter or telephone.*
Charges: *Send for details.*
Access: *BR: to Crewe, then 5 minutes by taxi to Centre. Car: via M6.*

Malpas

St Joseph's Retreat & Conference Centre
Tilston Road
Malpas
Cheshire SY14 7DD   Telephone: 0948 860416

Roman Catholic - Ecumenical

Run by the Sacred Heart Fathers, there are Ennegram and Myer Biggs workshops as well as courses on Celtic spirituality and weekends devoted to relaxation. A large and rambling old building with a modern wing and all amenities in a pretty village.

Open: *All year except Christmas and over New Year. Receives men,*

women, groups.
Rooms: *36 singles and 5 doubles are available.*
Facilities: *Limited disabled, conferences, garden, library, guest lounge, TV and pay phone.*
Spiritual Help: *Personal talks and group sharing.*
Guests Admitted to: *Chapel*
Meals: *Taken in guest dining room. Traditional food, with provision for vegetarian and special diets.*
Special Activities: *Send for brochure.*
Situation: *Quiet. In a village.*
Maximum Stay: *By arrangement.*
Bookings: *By letter or telephone.*
Charges: *£15 per day for individual retreats.*
Access: *BR: Whitchurch. Bus: National coach to Chester. Car: A41 between Chester and Whitchurch.*

CUMBRIA

Ambleside

Carlisle Diocesan Retreat & Conference Centre
Rydal Hall
Ambleside
Cumbria LA22 9LX   Telephone: 05394 32050

Anglican – Ecumenical

There is a relaxed atmosphere in this big Georgian house set in the heart of the Lake District, in a 30-acre estate with waterfalls and formal gardens. It is mainly used by groups, but individuals are welcomed and there is no pressure to join in any activities that may be taking place.

Open: *All year except December. Receives men, women, young people, families, groups and non-retreatants.*
Rooms: *10 single, 15 twin-bedded, plus a dormitory with bunks for 36, and camping facilities for youth groups.*
Facilities: *Disabled, chair lift, conferences, garden, library, guest lounge, TV and pay phone. Children welcome.*
Spiritual Help: *Personal talks, meditation and an opportunity to share the community life (worship, gardening, etc.).*
Guests Admitted to: *Unrestricted access to all areas, including chapel, work of the community.*

Meals: *Everyone eats together. Traditional food, with provision for vegetarian and special diets. Self-catering facilities in youth centre.*
Special Activities: *Planned programme of events. Send for the brochure.*
Situation: *Quiet, in the village and countryside.*
Maximum Stay: *2 weeks.*
Bookings: *By letter or telephone.*
Charges: *£21.85 per person per 24 hours, full board.*
Access: *BR: to Windermere. Bus: Ambleside. Car: via M6, Exit 40 from north, Exit 36 from south, then A591.*

Penrith

Friends Fellowship of Healing
Berrier Road, Greystoke
Lattendales, Penrith
Cumbria CA11 0UE   Telephone: 07684 83229

Quaker

The Fellowship is run in accordance with the principles of the Society of Friends (Quakers) but is open to all, irrespective of religious beliefs. The house is situated on the edge of Lakeland National Park, with easy access to the Lake District, Scotland and the North Pennines. The accommodation is comfortable, clean and pleasant.

Open: *April to October, and to groups for winter weekends. Receives men, women, young people, families, groups and non-retreatants.*
Rooms: *5 singles, 8 doubles.*
Facilities: *Conferences, garden, library, guest lounge and pay phone. Children welcomed. No pets.*
Spiritual Help: *Personal talks, group sharing, meditation.*
Guests Admitted to: *Unrestricted access.*
Meals: *Taken in the guest house. Traditional food, with provision for vegetarian and special diets.*
Special Activities: *Planned programme of events. Send for brochure.*
Situation: *Quiet, in the village and countryside just outside Lakeland National Park.*
Maximum Stay: *By arrangement.*
Bookings: *By letter or telephone.*
Charges: *Available on application.*
Access: *By rail, bus or car. See brochure, which has a good map.*

Pocklington

Madhyamaka Buddhist Centre
Kilnwick Percy Hall
Pocklington
Humberside YO4 2UF   Telephone: 0759 304832

Buddhist

The Centre is located in a very large Georgian country mansion built in 1784. Its aim is to preserve and promote the teachings and traditions of Tibetan Buddhism. About 50 residents ranging in age from 20 to 70 years regard this as their home. Some are ordained and all of them work and study together. Many are Buddhist teachers. There are group discussions, weekend and day courses throughout the year, plus a summer school. Other centres are in Bath, Buxton, and Ulverston.

Open: *All year. Receives men, women, young people, families, small groups, and non-retreatants.*
Rooms: *4 singles, 3 doubles, plus dormitories.*
Facilities: *Shrine room, garden, lake, park, library and pay phone. Children welcomed. No smoking or alcohol.*
Spiritual Help: *Personal talks, meditation, and monks, nuns and lay people willing to offer spiritual help.*
Guests Admitted to: *Unrestricted access. Guests may use shrine room and share the work of the community.*
Meals: *Everyone eats together and there are DIY facilities. Vegetarian wholefood.*
Special Activities: *There is a special programme, including working holidays. Send for brochure - and ask about their other centres in Bath, Buxton, and Ulverston.*
Situation: *Quiet, in the countryside.*
Maximum Stay: *Unlimited.*
Bookings: *By letter or telephone.*
Charges: *£19 single, £16.50 each in a double, £12 for a dormitory bed. All these charges are for full board per person.*
Access: *Please ask for directions when you are booking.*

Blackburn

Whalley Abbey
Blackburn Diocesan Conference & Retreat Centre
Whalley
Blackburn
Lancs. BB6 9SS   Telephone: 0254 822268

Anglican

Here is a great old former Cistercian abbey, steeped in history, which attracts many visitors every year. The programme of events includes holidays for walking and for senior citizens and such events as a craft fair and an open retreat on calligraphy and prayer. A place perhaps more for an active retreat than a meditative one.

Open: *All year except Christmas and New Year. Receives men, women, young people, groups and non-retreatants.*
Rooms: *18 bedrooms, sleeping 38 in total.*
Facilities: *Disabled, chair lift, conferences, garden, library, guest lounge, TV and pay phone. Children welcome.*
Spiritual Help: *Personal talks, meditation, directed retreats and resident chaplain.*
Guests Admitted to: *Unrestricted access to all areas, including chapel.*
Meals: *Everyone eats together. Traditional and wholefood with provision for vegetarian and special diets on request.*
Special Activities: *Send for brochure.*
Situation: *Quiet and peaceful environment, with beautiful tranquil gardens.*
Maximum Stay: *By arrangement.*
Bookings: *By letter.*
Charges: *£21.50 per day full board, £15.25 B&B, Weekend £43.50*
Access: *BR: to Blackburn. Bus: to Whalley. Car: via A59 to Whalley.*

Blackpool

Sisters of Marie Reparatrice
183 Newton Drive
Blackpool
Lancs. FY3 8NU   Telephone: 0253 391549

Roman Catholic

Open: *All year except Christmas and New Year. Receives men, women, groups and non-retreatants.*
Rooms: *8 singles.*
Facilities: *Conferences, garden, guest lounge, library, TV and pay phone.*
Spiritual Help: *Personal talks, meditation, days of recollection, and directed retreats – especially Ignation ones.*
Guests Admitted to: *Chapel, choir, work of the community.*
Meals: *Taken in the guest house. Traditional food, with provision for vegetarian and special diets by prior arrangement.*
Special Activities: *No planned programme of events.*
Situation: *Quiet, near shops, a park and the sea.*
Maximum Stay: *2 weeks.*
Bookings: *By letter.*
Charges: *On request.*
Access: *BR: to Blackpool North, then by taxi. Bus: No. 10. Car: to Blackpool.*

Carnforth

Monastery of Our Lady of Hyning
Warton
Carnforth
Lancs. LA5 9SE   Telephone: 0526 732684

Roman Catholic – Ecumenical/Inter-faith

Particularly suitable for private retreats, the Monastery is set in private grounds. In some rooms cheerful fires greet you in winter, while there is a peaceful and welcoming atmosphere everywhere. A barn has been converted into a church where guests may join the sisters in their daily schedule of prayer.

Open: *All year except for mid-July to late August. Receives men, women, young people from 6th form upwards, groups and non-retreatants.*
Rooms: *20 rooms, some single – 35 beds in all.*
Facilities: *Disabled, loop system for the deaf in the chapel and dining-room, conference room, garden, pasture land, library, guest telephone and laundry.*
Spiritual Help: *Personal talks, limited directed study, meditation.*
Guests Admitted to: *Chapel, choir, occasional community work.*
Meals: *Large dining-room and small dining-room serving mainly*

traditional food. Vegetarian and special diets catered for.
Special Activities: *Guests organise their own activities.*
Situation: *Quiet and in the countryside.*
Maximum Stay: *Normally a fortnight.*
Bookings: *By telephone or write to the Guestmistress.*
Charges: *Ask for the tariff. Students at a reduced rate. Rates for day groups by arrangement.*
Access: *BR: to Carnforth. Some local buses pass the gate. Car: via M6, Exit 35, and A6.*

LINCOLNSHIRE

Lincoln

Edward King House
The Old Palace
Lincoln LN2 1PU   Telephone: 0522 528778

Ecumenical

Once the palace of the Bishops of London, this retreat house stands in the shadow of one of England's greatest cathedrals. A spirituality programme is available as well as personal talks.

Open: *All year except Christmas. Receives men, women, young people, groups and non-retreatants.*
Rooms: *5 singles, 12 doubles.*
Facilities: *Conferences, garden, library, guest lounge, TV and pay phone. Children welcomed. Pets by arrangement.*
Spiritual Help: *Personal talks.*
Guests Admitted to: *Unrestricted access, except to kitchens and chapel.*
Meals: *Everyone eats together. Traditional food, with provision for vegetarian and special diets.*
Special Activities: *There is a spirituality programme for the year. Send for information.*
Situation: *In the city, close to the cathedral and most of the tourist attractions of Lincoln.*
Maximum Stay: *By arrangement.*
Bookings: *By letter or telephone.*
Charges: *Send for tariff.*
Access: *By public transport or car.*

Liverpool

**The Cenacle
7 Lance Lane
Wavertree
Liverpool L15 6TW**   Telephone: 051-722 2271

Roman Catholic

The Sisters of the Cenacle now offer individually directed retreats.
The retreat programme is wide ranging from counselling for wholeness and health to days especially for separated and divorced Catholic
men and women.

Open: *All year, except 15 December to 15 January. Receives men,
women, young people, groups.*
Rooms: *3 singles.*
Facilities: *Disabled, conferences, garden, library, pay phone.*
Spiritual Help: *Retreats, personal talks, meditation, directed study,
group sharing, days of prayer, and one-to-one spiritual direction.*
Guests Admitted to: *Chapel.*
Meals: *Very plain.*
Special Activities: *Some planned events.*
Situation: *Quiet, in town.*
Maximum Stay: *By arrangement.*
Bookings: *By letter or telephone.*
Charges: *£22 per 24 hrs. A day rate is available..*
Access: *BR: to Lime St station. Buses: Nos. 39, 54, 78, 79. Car: via
M62.*

MANCHESTER

Manchester

**The Cenacle Retreat House
28 Alexandra Road South,
Manchester M16 8HU**   Telephone: 061-226 1241

Roman Catholic

Open: *All year except Christmas and Easter. Receives men, women,
young people and groups.*
Rooms: *4 singles, 4 doubles.*

Facilities: *Small conferences, garden, library, guest lounge and pay phone.*
Spiritual Help: *Personal talks, group sharing and meditation. Individual quiet days with or without spiritual direction. There are prayer weeks and open door retreats as well.*
Guests Admitted to: *Chapel.*
Meals: *Everyone eats together. Traditional food, with provision for vegetarian and special diets.*
Special Activities: *Planned programme.*
Situation: *Quiet, in town - but opposite a park.*
Maximum Stay: *8 days normally.*
Bookings: *By letter with deposit and reference if first-timer.*
Charges: *£20 per person per day. Special prices for various events and courses.*
Access: *By rail, bus or car – directions supplied.*

MERSEYSIDE

New Brighton

Faith House
Yoga and Natural Health Centre
155 Victoria Road
New Brighton
Merseyside L45 9LB   Telephone: 051-639 9402

New Age

At Faith House yoga combines with aromatherapy body shaping techniques like Slendertone – not to mention facials – but then why not? It is certainly pleasant to be physically pampered when trying to relax and get rid of stress. There are mini health farm ' away days' and those not wishing to receive treatments can learn yoga or to meditate. For some this will seem a retreat and an escape from everyday worries. For others, not at all, as they will find it too much part of the mainstream of our contemporary culture. Be prepared for New Brighton – a rather damp and heavily Victorian town that has had its day.

Open: *All year. Receives men and women.*
Rooms: *A good number of singles and doubles are available as it is a large, reconditioned Victorian building.*
Facilities: *Gym, guest lounge, library, TV and payphone. No pets and*

no smoking.
Spiritual Help: *Yoga, meditation in guided classes.*
Guests Admitted to: *Unrestricted access.*
Meals: *Taken in large dining-room. Traditional food, special diets by arrangement.*
Special Activities: *Send for brochure.*
Situation: *Old seaside town.*
Maximum Stay: *By the day or the weekend.*
Bookings: *By telephone then letter.*
Charges: *From £32 per person per day. Ask what is included in price before booking.*
Access: *BR: to New Brighton. Bus: National Express to Liverpool, then local bus. Car: to New Brighton.*

Prescot

Loyola Hall Spirituality Centre
Warrington Road
Rainhill
Prescot
Merseyside L35 6NZ   Telephone: 051-426 4137

Roman Catholic – Interdenominational

This is a Jesuit retreat centre – and that usually means some hard work on prayer, personal introspection and spiritual growth if you want to undertake an individually guided retreat. In addition to this form of retreat, there are preached ones and special courses for those who work with young adults. The Centre itself is set in a park and consists of a combination of older buildings and functional new ones.

Open: *All year except Christmas week. Receives men, women, young people, groups and occasionally non-retreatants.*
Rooms: *46 single, 1 double, plus dormitories.*
Facilities: *Limited for disabled, but lift and loop system provided, conferences, park, library, guest lounge and pay phone.*
Spiritual Help: *Personal talks, group sharing on some retreats, meditation, directed study. Individually guided retreats in the tradition of St Ignatius Loyola. Courses on spiritual direction, prayer guidance.*
Guests Admitted to: *Unrestricted access.*
Meals: *Eaten in the guest dining rooms. Traditional food with provision for vegetarian and special diets.*

Special Activities: *Planned programme of events, including conferences, courses on spiritual direction, lecture programme, parish retreats. Send for brochure.*
Situation: *Quiet, in a village.*
Maximum Stay: *Up to 30 days depending on programme course undertaken.*
Bookings: *By letter or telephone*
Charges: *£25 per person per day, half price for students and unwaged.*
Access: *For rail and bus, see the programme. Car: via M62, Exit 7 to Prescot.*

NORTHUMBERLAND

Alnwick

The Friary
Society of St. Francis
Alnmouth
Alnwick
Northd. NE66 3NJ   Telephone: 0665 830213

Anglican

In addition to a programme which offers Myers Briggs workshops and courses in music, prayer, and spirituality, the Society of St Francis Friars offer support and accommodation for those who do not necessarily need a retreat of a religious nature but just a quiet break with a few days of peace. The Friary is situated on the coast, with beautiful Northumberland scenery and the Scottish borderlands near by.

Open: *All year. Receives men, women, families, groups and non-retreatants.*
Rooms: *8 singles, 1 doubles.*
Facilities: *Lift and shower for the disabled, small conferences, garden, library, TV, guest lounge and pay phone. Children welcome.*
Spiritual Help: *Personal talks if needed. Groups are encouraged to bring their own leaders.*
Guests Admitted to: *Chapel, work of the community.*
Meals: *Everyone eats together. Simple, traditional food with provision for vegetarian and special diets within reason.*
Special Activities: *Planned programme of events. Send for brochure.*

Situation: *Edge of village.*
Maximum Stay: *Usually from Tuesday to Saturday.*
Bookings: *By letter with SAE.*
Charges: *No fixed charge – about £15 per person per day.*
Access: *BR: to Alnmouth, 1 mile away. Bus: from Alnmouth to the Friary. Car: via A1.*

Berwick on Tweed

Marygate House
Holy Island
Berwick on Tweed
Northd. TD15 2SD   Telephone: 0289 89246

Ecumenical

Marygate House is situated on an island famous in Christian history and even today a place of pilgrimage and tourism. The centre is very quiet in winter but busy and popular in the summer. 'Love at first sight' is a common reaction of many guests. **Highly Recommended.**

Open: *All year except Christmas and New Year. Receives men, women, young people, families and groups.*
Rooms: *4 singles, 4 doubles, plus dormitories and arrangements in another house.*
Facilities: *Conferences, garden, library, guest lounge and pay phone. Children and pets welcomed.*
Spiritual Help: *Possible personal talks, group sharing, meditation and directed study.*
Guests Admitted to: *Unrestricted access to all areas, including chapel of silence.*
Meals: *Everyone eats together. Mostly simple, traditional food with provision for vegetarian and special diets. Facilities for silent meals, which are taken separately. No self-catering.*
Special Activities: *No planned programme of events.*
Situation: *Very quiet in winter, rather busy in summer.*
Maximum Stay: *2 weeks.*
Bookings: *By letter or telephone.*
Charges: *By donation.*
Access: *By rail or bus is possible but by car is best. Enquire when you book.*

Hexham

Throssel Hole Priory
Carrshield
Hexham
Northd. NE47 8AL   Telephone: 0434 345204

Buddhist

Since the time of Buddha many schools of Buddhism have developed. This monastery and centre of the Soto Zen School of Buddhism practises Serene Reflection Meditation. A variety of services for lay Buddhists is available, including naming ceremonies for children; cemetery plot and memorial services; and spiritual counselling by letter or telephone. There is a quarterly journal and a mail-order service offering books, taped lectures, meditation benches and cushions. Priests run retreats and make public talks outside the monastery. There is a sub-priory in Reading and about 30 affiliated Serene Meditation groups around the country.

Open: *All year except for pre-published periods. Receives men and women over 18 years. Families only received on specific weekends. Group educational visits from schools and colleges, by arrangement. Non-retreatants taken for tours of the monastery and may join in ceremony on the first Sunday of the month.*
Rooms: *Ceremony Hall - sleeps 30, sexes are separated.*
Facilities: *Garden, library, common room. Children welcome at the ceremony on the first Sunday of the month, but not for retreats.*
Spiritual Help: *Classes led by senior monk – private spiritual guidance on request. Full instruction given in meditation. Guidance is also given for private study/reflection.*
Guests Admitted to: *The ceremony hall, lay common-room and community work in most areas.*
Meals: *Taken together – vegetarian food.*
Special Activities: *By arrangement, with a special programme. Send for the brochure.*
Situation: *In the countryside.*
Maximum Stay: *3 months – longer by arrangement, but start your first stay with an introductory retreat.*
Bookings: *Application form.*
Charges: *By donation.*
Access: *BR: from Newcastle, or Carlisle to Hexham. Bus: from Newcastle to Hexham and Allendale. Car: via M6 or A1 to Bishop Auckland.*

Sheffield

Whirlow Grange Diocesan Conference Centre
Eccleshall Road South
Sheffield S11 9PZ   Telephone: 0742 363173

Anglican

The Centre occupies a grey-stone house on a rise on the outskirts of Sheffield, near Peak District beauty spots. The place is rather institutional, but it has comfortable rooms and facilities. There are healing seminars, sacred-dance group weekends and Franciscan directed retreats.

Open: *All year. Receives men, women, young people, families, groups and non-retreatants.*
Rooms: *20 singles, 10 twin-bedded rooms.*
Facilities: *Disabled, conferences, garden, bookstall, nearby park, library, guest lounge, TV and pay phone. Children welcomed.*
Spiritual Help: *Personal talks, group sharing, occasional meditation and directed study.*
Guests Admitted to: *Unrestricted access to all areas, including chapel.*
Meals: *Everyone eats together. Traditional and wholefood with provision for vegetarian.*
Special Activities: *Planned programme of events. Send for brochure.*
Situation: *Quiet and on the outskirts of the city. Peak District National Park within easy reach.*
Maximum Stay: *Any time within reason.*
Bookings: *By letter or telephone.*
Charges: *On application.*
Access: *By rail, bus or car (via A625).*

Ampleforth

Ampleforth Abbey
Ampleforth
N. Yorks. YO6 4EN   Telephone: 04393 225 (Monastery)
                                      04393 440 (The Grange)
                                      04393 405 (Redcar Farm)

Roman Catholic

The facilities at this large and busy monastery include single rooms for men guests. In addition there is the Grange, a large guest-house for men, and Redcar Farm – about three miles away – which offers a barn and a camping site, particularly suitable for young people. The Abbey is a good place to stay for personal study and reflection within the overall setting of a monastic community.

Open: *All year except Christmas and August. Receives men only at the monastery. The Grange receives men and women. It is closed during Easter week.*
Rooms: *10 singles for men in the monastery; 16 singles, 5 doubles in the Grange. Barn and camping at Redcar Farm.*
Facilities: *Church, guest lounge, library, bookstall, garden, plenty of places to walk.*
Spiritual Help: *No planned programme, but ask when you book.*
Guests Admitted to: *Abbey church, choir, monastery grounds.*
Meals: *Served in refectory for those staying in monastery; food also served at the Grange, with DIY for drinks. Self-service at Redcar Farm.*
Special Activities: *None.*
Situation: *Quiet, in the countryside.*
Maximum Stay: *By arrangement, but usually 4 nights.*
Bookings: *By letter to the Warden at the Grange or to the Guestmaster at the monastery.*
Charges: *Monastery by donation, Grange on application.*
Access: *BR and coach: to York, 23 miles away. Bus: ask about local public transport when you book. Car: via B1363 from York.*

*'Peace does not dwell in outward things, but within the soul' –
Fenelon*

Scarborough

Wydale Hall & Emmaus Centre
Brompton by Sawdon
Scarborough
N. Yorks. YO13 9DG   Telephone: 0723 859270

Interdenominational

An old house set in 14 acres with formal gardens with good views to the Yorkshire Wolds. Quiet Christian hospitality is on offer here with the purpose of trying to create a place where people can unwind, rest and, perhaps, draw nearer to God.

Open: *All year except first 2 weeks of January. Receives men, women, young people, families, groups and non-retreatants.*
Rooms: *10 singles, 16 doubles, plus family rooms, hostel, and dormitories.*
Facilities: *Disabled, conferences, chapel, camping, garden, park, library, guest lounge, bar, bookstall, TV and guest pay phone. Children welcome.*
Spiritual Help: *Personal talks, group sharing, meditation, and counselling.*
Guests Admitted to: *Unrestricted access to all areas, including chapel.*
Meals: *Everyone eats together. Traditional food, with provision for vegetarian and special diets.*
Special Activities: *Programme of events. Send for brochure.*
Situation: *Quiet and in the countryside. When guests are keeping silent, the staff endeavour to remain as quiet as possible and during meals only appear to clear and serve – guests' ease and comfort is the main priority.*
Maximum Stay: *Unlimited if beds available.*
Bookings: *By letter or telephone.*
Charges: *Send for details.*
Access: *BR: to Scarborough. Buses: from Scarborough. Car: Wydale Hall is 1 mile north of A170.*

'There is no wealth but life' – John Ruskin

Skipton

Parcevall Hall
Appletreewick
Skipton
N. Yorks. BD23 6DG   Telephone: 0756 720213

Anglican – Ecumenical

This is an Elizabethan manor-house whose interior is filled with oak and atmosphere. Legends and history abound, and the nine acres of garden are said to have been admired by the late Queen Mary. A traditional place for either a private retreat or participation in the programme of events.

Open: *All year. Receives men, women, and groups.*
Rooms: *5 singles, 11 doubles.*
Facilities: *Limited disabled in ground floor, conferences, garden, library, guest lounge, TV and pay phone.*
Spiritual Help: *Personal talks by prior arrangement.*
Guests Admitted to: *Chapel, garden.*
Meals: *Everyone eats together. Home cooking with provision for vegetarian and special diets.*
Special Activities: *Programme of events including massage and spirituality, Myer Briggs, painting and prayer. Send for brochure.*
Situation: *Very quiet, in the countryside.*
Maximum Stay: *1 week.*
Bookings: *By letter.*
Charges: *£27.50 per person per night.*
Access: *By car. Not accessible by public transport.*

Tadcaster

Hazlewood Castle
Tadcaster
N. Yorks. LS24 9NJ   Telephone: 0937 832738

Roman Catholic

Hazlewood Castle, formerly the home of the Vavasour family for over 800 years, is a bit forbidding, but the guest house in a converted stable-block is very comfortable. Situated in 70 acres of woodland, it is ideal for peaceful walks and reflection. The Carmelite Friars offer a varied programme of events and workshops, including preached retreats, Christian Zen meditation, personally directed sessions to develop your spirituality, and a course on lifestyle to give young adults the experience of a variety of prayer forms. No matter how many visitors may be milling around, the chapel remains a very peaceful place in which to meditate and pray.

Open: *All year except Christmas and New Year. Receives men, women, young people, families with children, groups, and non-retreatants.*
Rooms: *16 singles, 9 doubles and 6 rooms with 3 beds.*
Facilities: *Very limited for disabled, conferences, garden, park, library, guest lounge, TV and pay phone.*
Spiritual Help: *Personal talks, group sharing, meditation and directed study.*
Guests Admitted to: *Chapel, and work of the community.*
Meals: *Everyone eats together. Traditional food, with provision for vegetarian and special diets.*
Special Activities: *Programme with planned events. Send for brochure.*
Situation: *Surrounded by woodland.*
Maximum Stay: *By arrangement.*
Bookings: *By letter.*
Charges: *By arrangement.*
Access: *BR: to Leeds or York. Bus: No. 843 from York. Car: via A1, mid-way between Leeds and York on the A64.*

Thirsk

Holy Rood House & Community
10 Sowerby Road
Sowerby, Thirsk
N. Yorks. YO7 1HX   Telephone: 0845 522580

Ecumenical

Holy Rood House is run by the North of England Christian Healing Trust and all are welcome to visit. There are conferences during the year. For example, on healing and rural theology, and on mission studies
Open: *All year except Christmas. Receives men, women, young people, families, groups, and non-retreatants.*
Rooms: *2 singles, 1 double.*
Facilities: *Disabled chair lift, conferences, garden, library, guest*

lounge and pay phone. Children welcomed.
Spiritual Help: *Personal talks, group sharing, meditation, directed study, counselling, ministry of healing and laying on of hands.*
Guests Admitted to: *Unrestricted access. Chapel. Work of community.*
Meals: *Everyone eats together. Plain cooking with provision for vegetarians if required. DIY for tea and coffee.*
Special Activities: *No planned programme, but some events during the year.*
Situation: *Quiet and in the village.*
Maximum Stay: *1 week.*
Bookings: *By letter or telephone.*
Charges: *Please enquire when booking.*
Access: *BR: to Thirsk $1^1/_2$ miles away. Bus: to Thirsk, then 10 - minute walk. Car: via A61 to B1448, or A19 and A168.*

Whitby

St Oswald's Pastoral Centre
Woodlands Drive
Sleights
nr. Whitby
N. Yorks. YO21 1RY   Telephone: 0947 810496

Anglican

The sisters welcome guests to conducted retreats, individually guided retreats, and for private quiet time for rest and study. The facilities for guests are in a small complex of buildings set in beautiful Yorkshire surroundings.

Open: *All year except Christmas and August. Receives men, women, young people, families, groups and non-retreatants.*
Rooms: *6 singles, 2 doubles.*
Facilities: *Garden, library, guest lounge, TV and guest telephone.*
Spiritual Help: *Personal talks, meditation, group sharing, directed study.*
Guests Admitted to: *Unrestricted access except to community quarters.*
Meals: *Everyone eats together. Traditional food, with provision for vegetarian and special diets. Self-catering available.*
Special Activities: *Planned programme of events. Send for the brochure.*

Situation: *Very quiet, in the countryside near to the moors.*
Maximum Stay: *Normally 10 days.*
Bookings: *By letter or telephone.*
Charges: *On request.*
Access: *By car is best.*

York

St Bede's Monastery & Pastoral Centre
21 & 23 Blossom Street
York YO2 2AQ   Telephone: 0904 610443   (Monastery)
                                        0904 610446 (Pastoral Centre)

Roman Catholic

St. Bede's was founded in 1987 as a joint venture by the Middlesborough Diocese and the Ampleforth monks. It is a base for ecumenical work right in the heart of York and next door to Bar Convent Museum which is well worth a visit and the Youth Centre. All the rooms are modern in style with practical furnishings and there is a pretty small garden at the rear which is very pleasant. The programme is that of a pastoral centre and so there are events and talks throughout most of the year. The spiritual growth programmes include healing courses. A friendly and welcoming place in the heart of a great and hospitable city.

Open: *All year except Christmas. Receives men only.*
Rooms: *4 singles.*
Facilities: *Chapel, non-residential conferences, garden, TV, book-stall.*
Spiritual Help: *Personal talks, sharing in community prayer, daily Mass.*
Guests Admitted to: *Unrestricted access.*
Meals: *Traditional food, eaten together.*
Special Activities: *Programme of events. Holistic and Myer Briggs weekends, Enneagram and spirituality, and a workshop on discernment are among the events on offer. Send for brochure.*
Situation: *Busy and in the city, but once inside quite peaceful.*
Maximum Stay: *No restrictions.*
Bookings: *By letter.*
Charges: *By donation.*
Access: *By rail, bus or car to York.*

Ilkley

Myddelton Lodge
Langbar Road
Ilkley
W. Yorks. LS29 OEB   Telephone: 0943 607887

Roman Catholic – Non-denominational

The centre faces south, overlooking the town of Ilkley and the Ilkley Moors, with easy access to the Dales. A range of retreats is on offer, including those for schools and for the disabled, plus their parents and helpers.

Open: *All year. Receives individuals and all groups.*
Rooms: *20 singles, 20 doubles.*
Facilities: *Disabled, conferences, chapel, garden, park, library, guest lounge, TV and pay phone. Children welcomed. Pets permitted.*
Spiritual Help: *Personal talks, group sharing, meditation, directed study.*
Guests Admitted to: *Unrestricted access to all areas, including chapel.*
Meals: *Everyone eats together. Home-cooking, with provision for vegetarian and special diets.*
Special Activities: *Planned programme of events. Send for brochure.*
Situation: *Very quiet, good grounds, beautiful countryside, good walking. The centre has a welcoming and homely atmosphere.*
Maximum Stay: *By arrangement..*
Bookings: *By letter or telephone.*
Charges: *£22 per person per 24 hours.*
Access: *By rail, bus or car. Ask for details when applying.*

'Glance at the sun. See the moon and stars. Gaze at the beauty of earth's greenings. Now, think' – Hildegard of Bingen

Wales

Corwen

Coleg Y Groes
The College
Corwen
Clwyd LL21 OAU   Telephone: 0490 412169

Church in Wales

Two women deacons in the Church of Wales and a pastoral counsellor run this big, comfortable house nestling in a quiet spot between church and mountainside near the River Dee. There are counselling and prayer for healing, and individual needs are catered for in an environment that aims to convey the peace of Christ.

Open: *Most of the year. Receives men, women, young people, families, small groups and non-retreatants.*
Rooms: *6 singles, doubles are available.*
Facilities: *Garden, books to read, guest lounge and TV. Children welcome, dogs only by prior arrangement.*
Spiritual Help: *Personal talks, guided retreats for individuals.*
Guests Admitted to: *Guest accommodation and garden.*
Meals: *Taken in the guest house. Varied home-cooking, with provision by arrangement for vegetarian and special diets but not for vegans. Meals served on tray in room for those keeping silence.*
Special Activities: *None.*
Situation: *Quiet in a small town.*
Maximum Stay: *Unrestricted.*
Bookings: *By telephone or letter.*
Charges: *Send for price list - ranges from £14 per person per day to £95 for a week.*
Access: *BR: nearest station is Wrexham. Infrequent bus service. Car: house is just off A5.*

Corwen

Vajraloka Buddhist Meditation Centre
Blaenddol House
Treddol
Corwen
Clwyd LL21 OEN   Telephone: 0490 81406

Buddhist

Apart from running a few special events during the year for women, Vajraloka is principally a men's Buddhist centre. Its sole purpose is to provide facilities for the practice of meditation, and it is open to newcomers as well as the more experienced meditators. If you have done a month or so of meditation, then you can come on most of the courses here. The Centre is set in the beautiful countryside of North Wales and it is a very peaceful place. Remember to bring loose clothing for meditation.

Open: *All year round. Receives men, occasionally women at special events.*
Rooms: *7 singles, 3 doubles, dormitory.*
Facilities: *Shrine room, garden, pay phone.*
Spiritual Help: *Meditation, directed study, group sharing, personal talks. On all retreats the community teaches a creative approach in meditation workshops.*
Guests Admitted to: *Shrineroom. The library by arrangement*
Meals: *Everyone eats together. Wholefood, vegetarian.*
Special Activities: *Planned programme of events – send for the brochure. Some events may be restricted, depending on a person's experience. One of very few single-sex Buddhist meditation centres in Europe where meditation continues throughout the year.*
Situation: *Very quiet, beautiful countryside.*
Maximum Stay: *By arrangement.*
Bookings: *By letter or telephone.*
Charges: *See programme.*
Access: *By car, but ask when you book, as the route is a little complicated.*

Corwen

The Vajrakuta Buddhist Study Centre for Men
Blaenddol House
Treddol
Corwen
Clwyd LL21 OEN   Telephone: 0490 81406

Buddhist

The Vajrakuta Buddhist Study Centre for Men is a Dharama study centre of the Friends of the Western Buddhist Order with a community team dedicated to the study of this spiritual practice. It is linked to the Vajraloka centre about half a mile down the road. The study centre has a hermitage caravan available for a solitary retreat which, although located within the grounds, offers silence and no intrusions.

Open: *All year, receives men.*
Rooms: *Mostly in shared rooms, sometimes a single is available. Bed linen is provided. Hermitage caravan with all facilities in grounds for a solitary retreat.*
Facilities: *Garden, library.*
Spiritual Help: *Personal talks, meditation practice, directed study practice by resident Dharma study community.*
Guests Admitted to: *Shrineroom.*
Meals: *Everyone eats together. All meals are vegetarian or vegan.*
Special Activities: *A short but excellent programme of open seminars for men which may include such topics as the White Lotus Sutra, the Nature of Existence based on the text of Sangharakshita, and the Bodhisattva's Way of Life. Other seminars for mitras and special retreats and seminars for members of FWBO are included in the programme..*
Situation: *Lost in green hills with ample grounds and beautiful surrounding countryside..*
Maximum Stay: *By arrangement.*
Bookings: *By letter or telephone.*
Charges: *Suggested nightly rates, depending on your income: retreats from £22 to £14.50, guests from £18.50 to £11. Hermitage caravan rate from £101.50 to £77 per week which includes food provision for one person.*
Access: *Ask for directions when you book.*

Hawarden

Poor Clares Monastery
Ty Man Duw
Upper Aston Hall Lane
Hawarden
Clwyd CH5 3EN　　　　　Telephone 0244 531029

Roman Catholic

The community offers a warm welcome for people who want rest and prayer. Rooms are comfortable with nice facilities.

Open: *All year. Receives women, married couples, priests, young*

people with a leader, and groups, but no holiday makers.
Rooms: *4 singles, 2 doubles.*
Facilities: *Conferences, garden, guest lounge, TV and telephone. No pets.*
Spiritual Help: *Personal talks, meditation, directed study.*
Guests Admitted to: *Chapel.*
Meals: *Taken in the guesthouse. Traditional food with provision for vegetarians. DIY facilities.*
Special Activities: *No planned programme of events.*
Situation: *Quiet. In a village*
Maximum Stay: *Unlimited*
Bookings: *By letter.*
Charges: *By donation.*
Access: *BR: to Chester. Ask about buses when you book.*

St Asaph

St Beuno's Spiritual Exercise Centre
St Asaph
Tremeirchion
Clwyd LL17 OAS   Telephone: 0745 583444

Roman Catholic

This is a leading Jesuit centre of spirituality for the teaching and study of the spiritual exercises of St Ignatius Loyola for Christians from all over the world. These famous exercises are a series of Scripture-based, Christ-centred meditations and contemplations designed to help each retreatant to discover his or her 'hidden self'. There are courses designed to last six or eight days, others which are given in eight-day periods over three months, and the full course of spiritual exercises involving a continuous period of some 30 days. The Ignatian exercises are among the most famous and rigorous of all spiritual retreats. You should first read up about this form of retreat and perhaps discuss it with your spiritual adviser or priest before deciding to go. **Highly Recommended.**

Open: *As published in programme, but closes during January. Receives men and women.*
Rooms: *45 singles.*
Facilities: *Limited for disabled, garden, library, guest lounge and card phone.*
Spiritual Help: *Group sharing, meditation, directed study. 3 month*

courses in apostolic spirituality for Christians, 30 day retreats, 2 month training courses.
Guests Admitted to: *Unrestricted access.*
Meals: *Traditional food, with provision for vegetarian and special diets.*
Special Activities: *Send for brochure.*
Situation: *Very quiet in the countryside.*
Maximum Stay: *The 3 month course.*
Bookings: *By letter.*
Charges: *Suggest an offering of £25 per day.*
Access: *By rail to Rhyl, otherwise by car.*

DYFED

Llandeilo

Tipi Valley
Cwmdn
Llandeilo
Dyfed   Telephone: None

New Age – North American Indian

Tipi Valley is a scattered community of 60 or so families living in tipi lodges of the type used by North American Indians. This area of Wales is truly rural in a secret, rocky, green way, with beautiful tracts of bracken, deep forest valleys and lanes without traffic. Rain is never very far away. Tipi Valley qualifies as a place of retreat because of its isolation, lack of obvious structure, prevailing silence, guest lodge and rituals that are more or less based on American Indian spirituality. These rituals consist of simple communal chanting and dancing to earth spirits. There can be much nakedness, so if you are over-modest then be warned. The sweat-lodge is a low willow-frame, covered in cloth, that works like a pitch-dark sauna. It is incredibly hot and you can only bear it if you keep chanting. When you have had enough, run a short distance to a mountain pool and dive in – the effect is purging, therapeutic and rather magical. To stay here you must come equipped for camping. The guest lodge provides cover and a cooking-hearth. You will be expected to cut and gather reeds for the tipi floor, collect wood, and cook in rotation with others. Bring rain-gear and good boots. While Tipi Valley is not for the unfit or the highly conservative, it is also not exclusively a young people's place. All ages seem equally attracted to this alternative lifestyle, which is unique in Britain. But such places as Tipi Valley drift into being and vanish again, so you may find only the green hills and nothing more- but you will have enjoyed a delightful walk which in itself can be a way of meditation and retreat to inner peace.

Open: *All year. Receives men, women, groups and families, including children.*
Rooms: *Sleeping places are arranged when you arrive. A large tipi serves as the guest lounge.*
Facilities: *No modern facilities at all.*
Spiritual Help: *Chanting, Indian sweat-lodges, rituals linked to nature.*
Guests Admitted to: *Everywhere in valley, while respecting the privacy of others.*
Meals: *Bring your own food. Most of the resident community is vegetarian.*
Special Activities: *No planned programme.*
Situation: *7 miles from nowhere, among hills in a hidden valley. Very quiet and deeply rural.*
Maximum Stay: *Probably as long as you like.*
Bookings: *None required.*
Charges: *None.*
Access: *Bus or train to Swansea, then local bus to Llandeilo. From there walk, hitch, or take a taxi 7 miles to Cwmdn. Rest awhile because next you climb 5 miles into the hills. Local residents will give you directions if you get lost.*

Rhandirmwyn

Nantymwyn Retreat of the Visitation
Rhandirmwyn
Dyfed SA20 0NR   Telephone: 0550 6247

Anglican – Ecumenical

This old Welsh farmhouse is run as a retreat centre by an Anglican priest and his wife for all who wish to make a private retreat in a warm, welcoming and relaxing environment. Occasionally parish groups also stay here. Divine Office daily and the Eucharist every other day help to maintain a spiritual atmosphere for all. There is a smallholding and garden, in which retreatants are welcome to help if they want. In this way, you can achieve a balance between prayer and physical work – a combination that contemplative monasteries have found over the centuries brings a deepening of spirituality. The house is in a very beautiful part of the Cambrian Mountains and the surroundings are delightful – but if all you are after is a cheap holiday, then go somewhere else.

Open: *All year. Receives men and women.*
Rooms: *Can accommodate 6, more if absolutely necessary.*
Facilities: *Chapel, garden, smallholding, library, lounge and TV.*
Spiritual Help: *Personal talks if required. Some directed study if you ask.*
Guests Admitted to: *More or less unrestricted access.*
Meals: *Everyone eats together, dining from garden produce.*
Special Activities: *No planned programme.*
Situation: *In the countryside, very peaceful.*
Maximum Stay: *By arrangement.*
Bookings: *By letter.*
Charges: *Please enquire when you write.*
Access: *By car via A40 or A483 to Llandovery, then up Towy Valley.*

GWENT

Monmouth

Society of the Sacred Cross
Tymawr Convent
Lydart
Monmouth
Gwent NP5 4RN   Telephone: 0600 860244

Anglican

Lots of vegetables and fruit are grown by the sisters here, so the food is fresh, if plain, and you will feel well looked after in this house, which has views across a lush valley of green fields in the Wye Valley.

Open: *Almost all year - enquire as to current closed weeks. Receives men, women, young people, groups and non-retreatants.*
Rooms: *8 singles, 3 doubles.*
Facilities: *Chapel, garden, park, library, guest lounge and guest telephone. Children welcomed. Pets permitted only by special arrangement.*
Spiritual Help: *Personal talks, counselling, directed study, reflexology.*

Guests Admitted to: *Chapel, choir, work of the community.*
Meals: *Very plain food taken in the guest house, with provision for vegetarian and special diets. Self-catering facilities.*
Special Activities: *No planned programme of events.*
Situation: *Very quiet, in the countryside.*
Maximum Stay: *1 month.*
Bookings: *By letter or telephone.*
Charges: *£15 per person per night, full board; £7.50 per night, self-catering.*
Access: *By car is best. House is 4 miles south of Monmouth.*

GWYNEDD

Dolgellau

Carmelite Monastery
Cader Road
Dolgellau
Gwynedd LL40 1SH   Telephone: 0341 422546

Roman Catholic

Open: *All year, except when on retreat themselves. Receives women, men, young people, non-retreatants.*
Rooms: *Only limited space, but guests who wish to make a retreat can use a bungalow. This is also available to women considering the Carmelite religious life.*
Facilities: *Small garden, TV on request, books to read, telephone.*
Spiritual Help: *Personal talks if requested.*
Guests Admitted to: *Chapel.*
Meals: *DIY facilities.*
Special Activities: *No special activities or planned programme.*
Situation: *Quiet and in the countryside, with opportunities for walks in the mountains.*
Maximum Stay: *1 week.*
Bookings: *By telephone but confirm by letter.*
Charges: *On request.*
Access: *By rail to Machynlleth station, then by bus or car.*

'He leads me beside the waters of peace' – Psalm 23

Llanrwst

Christian Conference, Retreat & Holiday Centre
Pencraig Arthur
Llanddoged
Llanrwst
Gwynedd LL26 ODZ   Telephone: 0492 640959

Interdenominational

The Reverend John Farrimond, a Methodist minister, who trained in
the Ignation Schoool of spirituality, offers personal talks and guided
retreats. The house is located on the edge of Snowdonia National Park
so there is excellent walking.

Open: *By arrangement. Receives men, women, young people, fami-*
lies, groups and non-retreatants.
Rooms: *1 single, 6 doubles, 1 caravan.*
Facilities: *Conferences, garden, guest lounge, TV and guest tel-*
ephone. Children welcomed. Pets only by prior arrangement.
Spiritual Help: *Personal talks, spiritual direction, individually*
guided retreats.
Guests Admitted to: *Unrestricted access.*
Meals: *Self-catering.*
Special Activities: *Send for brochure.*
Situation: *Very quiet in the countryside.*
Maximum Stay: *By arrangement.*
Bookings: *By telephone or letter.*
Charges: *By arrangement, but modest rates.*
Access: *By car only.*

Pwllheli

'Croesfryn'
Bryncroes
nr. Sarn
Pwllheli
Gwynedd LL53 8EY   Telephone: 071-359 1394
                                        for enquiries

Buddhist

This retreat centre belongs strictly to the Mahayana Buddhist tradition of Lama Tsong Kha Pa (Gelug). There is a resident Tibetan monk

who is a qualified meditation master, and he can give personal guidance in Buddhist meditation by prior arrangement.

Open: *All year. Receives men, women, young people, families, groups and religious.*
Rooms: *About 10 singles, plus dormitories, hermitage, hostel and caravans.*
Facilities: *Camping, garden, library, guest lounge and TV.*
Spiritual Help: *Personal talks, group sharing, meditation and directed study.*
Guests Admitted to: *Shrine room and the work of the community.*
Meals: *DIY facilities only.*
Special Activities: *Group retreats at Christmas, Easter and in the summer.*
Situation: *Very quiet and in the countryside. Distant views across Lleyn Peninsula.*
Maximum Stay: *By negotiation.*
Bookings: *By letter to Jamyang Meditation Centre, 10 Finsbury Park Road, London N4 2JZ.*
Charges: *Low.*
Access: *By car.*

POWYS

Brecon

Coleg Trefeca
Trefeca
Talgarth
Brecon
Powys LD3 OPP   Telephone: 0874 711423

Presbyterian Church of Wales

The centre consists of a group of 18th-century buildings and a modern block, standing in five acres of grounds set in the Brecon Beacons National Park. Short retreats, ecumenical activities, holiday weeks for older folk and young people are on offer, as well as courses in Myers-Briggs, Christian pastoral counselling, study for lay preachers, and Jewish-Christian consultation. The programme brochure is in both Welsh and English. A good place for a stimulating retreat, mixing with other like-minded people.

Open: *All year. Receives men, women, young people, families, groups and non-retreatants.*
Rooms: *19 twin-bedded.*
Facilities: *Conferences, garden, library, guest lounge, TV and guest pay phone. Children and pets welcomed.*
Spiritual Help: *Personal talks if requested.*
Guests Admitted to: *Unrestricted access.*
Meals: *Everyone eats together. Very plain food, with provision for vegetarian and special diets.*
Special Activities: *Planned programme, though groups, churches and secular organisations may follow their own programme.*
Situation: *Very quiet, in an area of outstanding natural beauty. 10 miles from Brecon and an ideal centre for those who wish to walk, climb, pony-trek, or simply admire the views.*
Maximum Stay: *Unrestricted.*
Bookings: *By telephone but confirm by letter.*
Charges: *Very reasonable, varying according to personal situation.*
Access: *By car.*

Brecon

Llangasty Retreat House
Brecon
Powys LD3 7PJ   Telephone: 087 484 250

Anglican

This isolated and large stone house, hidden away from roads and the busy world, is run by the Sisters of Charity. It is comfortable, cheerful and overlooks a marvellous lake.

Open: *All year except mid-December to 1 February. Receives men, women, young people, families, groups and non-retreatants.*
Rooms: *10 singles, 3 doubles.*
Facilities: *Conferences, garden, library, guest lounge, direct-dialling telephone. Children welcomed.*
Spiritual Help: *Personal talks.*
Guests Admitted to: *Unrestricted access. Chapel.*
Meals: *Everyone eats together. Traditional food, with provision for vegetarian.*
Special Activities: *None.*
Situation: *Very quiet, in the countryside.*
Maximum Stay: *By arrangement.*

Bookings: *By telephone but confirm by letter.*
Charges: *Upon application.*
Access: *By car to Brecon.*

Builth Wells

The Skreen
Erwood
Builth Wells
Powys LD2 3SJ

Telephone: 098 23 210

Ecumenical

The Skreen has long enjoyed a reputation for being a place where you may search, explore, share, be silent, worship and be at peace with yourself. A new centre is opening soon and it will focus on the study and practice of contemplative and creative theology, spirituality, and liturgy. The house is beautifully situated above the River Wye, near a small village. **Highly Recommended.**

Open: *For organised courses only. Receives men and women.*
Rooms: *2 singles, 5 doubles.*
Facilities: *Chapel, garden, library and guest lounge.*
Spiritual Help: *Personal talks, meditation, directed study.*
Guests Admitted to: *Chapel.*
Meals: *Everyone eats together. Wholefood, with provision for vegetarian and special diets.*
Special Activities: *Planned programme of events. Send for brochure.*
Situation: *Quiet.*
Maximum Stay: *As per programme.*
Bookings: *By letter or telephone.*
Charges: *Upon application.*
Access: *Car-route directions in the brochure.*

*'Silence of the heart practised with wisdom will see
a lofty depth and the ear of the silent mind
will hear untold wonders'*

Hesychius of Jerusalem

Bleddfa
Knighton

The Bleddfa Trust
Centre for Caring and the Arts
The Old School, Bleddfa
Nr. Knighton
Powys   Telephone: 054 47 540

Interdenominational

Here is an exciting and different place to go for spiritual and personal
development. Bleddfa does not fit into any 'retreat' category but is a
special place well worth a day visit or attending one of the workshops.
John Hencher, who runs the monthly workshops on self-knowledge
and self-development, is called 'Director of Caring', which seems a
wonderfully thought-provoking title to possess in this age of materi-
alism. These expertly run workshops are meant to open new horizons
of spirituality and self-awareness. For example, they might be on
'light' or 'hope', and from these simple words the day unfolds at
Bleddfa into a new awakening of the spirit, leading to better insight
into yourself. Such days of group sharing are especially useful for
those who may think that they have already fully explored the creative
dimensions of their personal spirituality. The Bleddfa Trust runs a
gallery in the Old School which has gained a national reputation for
the quality of its art and craft exhibitions, all of which are mounted
with great sensitivity by the director, John Cupper. There is a small
book-and-gift shop and you may take tea in a light, new inside room
or seated outside in a charming herb garden. **Highly Recommended.**

Open: *All year. Receives men, women, young people, families.*
Rooms: *Guests stay in local B&B accommodation.*
Facilities: *Various meeting rooms, Old School gallery, bookshop.*
Spiritual Help: *A monthly workshop is held on the first Saturday of
each month from 10.30 a.m. to 5.00 p.m. Personal talks, group
sharing, meditation. A 'listening post' function has been set up for
those in need of someone to just listen to them- a rare and valuable
help in these hurried times.*
Guests Admitted to: *Centre and gardens.*
Meals: *Bring your own food. At some events food is served but needs
to be booked in advance.*
Special Activities: *Send for brochure.*
Situation: *In wonderful countryside with distant views.*
Maximum Stay: *For length of course or events.*

Bookings: *By letter.*
Charges: *Per activity or event.*
Access: *By car only.*

Llangunllo

The Samatha Centre
Greenstreete
Llangunllo
Powys LD7 1SP   Telephone 061-881 0038

Buddhist (Therevada Tradition)

Greenstreete Farm was purchased by the Samatha Trust in 1987 for use as a residential meditation centre. It consists of a big farmhouse set in 88 acres of land. The setting is lovely, with views in all directions of green pastures and rising hills. There are streams and woods with secluded places where small huts have been built for use by meditators wanting solitude. Everyone is welcome here to learn this gentle and effective way of meditation. There are regular classes for the more experienced and some for beginners.

Open: *Most weekends but enquire first. Receives men and women.*
Rooms: *8 singles, 4 in huts.*
Facilities: *Shrine hall, library.*
Spiritual Help: *Personal talks, group work, directed study, and individual instruction on Samatha meditation.*
Guests Admitted to: *Unrestricted access everywhere.*
Meals: *Everyone eats together. Traditional food. Provision for vegetarians, and special diets, within reason.*
Special Activities: *Send or telephone for the programme. Beginners go to occasional introductory weekend courses in meditation practice and there are Sunday afternoon meditation classes as well.*
Situation: *Deep in the countryside on a green hill and very peaceful.*
Maximum Stay: *By arrangement.*
Bookings: *By letter or telephone.*
Charges: *£15 per day or £100 per week.*
Access: *BR: to Llangunllo station which is less than a mile away. It is an easy walk down a lane and up a small hill to the Centre. By car from Knighton in Powys to Llangunllo, then through the village and the Centre will be seen on a hill to the left. The entrance is sign-posted.*

Scotland

Hawick

The Chisholme Institute
Chisholme House
Roberton
Nr. Hawick
Roxburghshire TD9 7PH   Telephone: 0450 88215

Beshara School of Esoteric Education

Beshara means 'good news'. It is reputed to be the word the angel
Gabriel used when he announced the coming of Christ to Mary. The
idea of the Beshara School is to strive towards an understanding of the
unity of existence. This study of spiritual awareness is quite demanding as it encompasses many traditions, ranging from Judaic, Christian
and Far Eastern to classical texts. The house itself is Georgian, the
accommodation almost luxuriously comfortable, and the food imagi-
natively prepared. The staff and students are helpful, relaxed and
welcoming. Courses run from 10 days to six months. Guests can
choose to participate in the end-of-day meditational practice where
names of gods are chanted. For those who are genuinely spiritually
minded and who do not want anything denominational, church
structured, or based on a single spiritual tradition, then Chisholme is
a good place to try.

Open: *All year. Receives men, women, young people, families,
groups and non-retreatants.*
Rooms: *2 singles, 6 doubles, dormitory, special bedroom for the
disabled and another 2 under construction.*
Facilities: *Disabled, camping by arrangement.*
Spiritual Help: *Personal talks, meditation, directed study.*
Guests Admitted to: *Unrestricted access in main building, medita-
tion room.*
Meals: *Everyone eats together. French and Turkish food, some
home-produced. Vegetarians and medical diets only catered for.*
Special Activities: *Annual open day, lectures. Some people come just
to work in the large garden. Brochure available.*
Situation: *Very quiet, in the countryside.*
Maximum Stay: *By arrangement.*
Bookings: *By letter.*
Charges: *£15 per person per day. Long stay charges on application.*
Access: *BR: to Carlisle, then by bus. Bus: to Hawick, then by taxi.
Car: via M6, A7.*

Hawick

Whitchester Christian Guest House & Retreat Centre
Borthaugh
Hawick
Roxburgh TD9 7LN   Telephone: 0450 77477

Interdenominational

Open: *All year. Receives men, women, families, groups and non-retreatants.*
Rooms: *2 single, 8 doubles.*
Facilities: *Disabled, conferences, large gardens, library, guest lounge, TV and pay phone. Children welcomed, pets permitted by arrangement.*
Spiritual Help: *Personal talks, meditation, directed study, shared worship.*
Guests Admitted to: *Unrestricted access to all areas, including chapel.*
Meals: *Taken in the guest house. Wholefood, with provision for vegetarians and special diets.*
Special Activities: *Staff's daily worship is open to guests. No special programme.*
Situation: *Very quiet.*
Maximum Stay: *By arrangement.*
Bookings: *By letter or telephone.*
Charges: *Retreatants £22 per day full board. Others £36.80 per day full board.*
Access: *By rail, bus or car (A7).*

CENTRAL

Dunblane

Scottish Churches House
Kirk Street
Dunblane
Perthshire FK15 OAJ   Telephone: 0786 823588

Interdenominational

This is a conference centre, belonging to all the mainline churches in Scotland, but daily retreats are organised for individuals. The Centre consists of a row of converted and renovated 18th century cottages and a church along two sides of the Cathedral square. The atmosphere is quiet and homely.

Open: *All year except mid-July to mid-August. Receives men, women, groups and non-retreatants over 18 years of age.*
Rooms: *12 singles, 21 doubles.*
Facilities: *Conferences, garden, library, guest lounge, direct-dialling pay phone.*
Spiritual Help: *Group sharing, personal talks, meditation, corporate and personal retreats.*
Guests Admitted to: *Unrestricted access to all areas, including chapel.*
Meals: *Everyone eats together. Traditional food with provision for vegetarian and special diets.*
Special Activities: *Planned programme of events. Send for leaflet.*
Situation: *Quiet but in a city.*
Maximum Stay: *Open.*
Bookings: *By telephone or letter.*
Charges: *£22.50 per day, £11 B&B.*
Access: *By rail, bus or car.*

DUMFRIES and GALLOWAY

Langholm

Kagyu Samye Ling Tibetan Centre
Eskdalemuir
nr. Langholm
Dumfriesshire DG13 OQL   Telephone: 03873 232

Buddhist

The Centre was the first British Tibetan monastery to be set up following the Cultural Revolution. Lamas regularly visit in summer and guests may request interviews. Unless on retreat, guests stay in separate accommodation from the retreat centre. All guests may participate in temple meditation, prayer and work. The atmosphere is lively and warm. There is a full-time community, consisting mostly of young people who obviously derive peace and pleasure from being at the Centre and lend the place an atmosphere of calm. They work at the dairy and farm. There is also a foundry, weaving and painting shops, a pottery and printing press. The Centre leaves one with an impression of New Age ideas combined with very genuine Tibetan Buddhism. A stimulating place, there is plenty to do and a wonderful landscape to explore. In 1992, Holy Island near Arran in the Firth of Clyde was purchased by the Samye Ling Centre for the solitude it offered as an ideal venue for prayer and meditation. Renovations to the buildings and pier have already started along with a project to plant 4,500 broadleaf trees. **Highly Recommended.**

Open: *All year. Receives men, women, young people, single- parent families and non-retreatants. Disabled received by arrangement.*
Rooms: *6 singles, 8 doubles, 5 dormitories, plus space for tents, owner-occupied caravans.*
Facilities: *Conferences, camping, garden, small library and pay phone. Children welcome.*
Spiritual Help: *Personal talks, informal group-sharing encouraged, meditation. Weekend courses in therapy, massage, holistic practice. Also 10-year study courses divided into 3 blocks. Full retreats by arrangement. Courses also run for 2 weeks at Christmas, 1 month at Easter and 3 months over summer (July–September).*
Guests Admitted to: *Temple, shrine room, craft work of the community, building projects and general projects. Guests are asked to work for 2 hours a day.*
Meals: *Everyone eats together. The food is vegetarian, with provision for special diets by arrangement.*
Special Activities: *Planned programme of events. Send for the brochure.*
Situation: *Quiet, busy in summer.*
Maximum Stay: *As arranged.*
Bookings: *By letter or telephone.*
Charges: *Send for details.*
Access: *All routes difficult. BR and bus to Lockerbie, then by taxi for 14 miles.*

Edinburgh

House of Prayer
8 Nile Grove
Edinburgh EH10 4RF   Telephone: 031-447 1772

Christian – Interdenominational

Located in one of Scotland's few moneyed and middle-class suburban areas, the House of Prayer embraces all denominations and tries to promote an unsensational Christian spiritualism. Meditation is encouraged and there is a chapel with regular services. Rooms are clean and bright, and surrounding the house is a fine garden. This place is more for the traditionally inclined older Christian than the young seeker – but there are plenty of up-to-date courses in the programme, from 30-day retreats and prayer days for women, to lectures on that most gifted of poets, Gerard Manley Hopkins.

Open: *All year. Receives men, women, groups up to 10. No children.*
Rooms: *10 singles.*
Facilities: *Chapel, conferences, garden, library, guest lounge and guest telephone.*
Spiritual Help: *Personal talks, group sharing, meditation, directed study, chapel services.*
Guests Admitted to: *Unrestricted access.*
Meals: *Everyone eats together. Traditional food. Vegetarians catered for by prior arrangement. No special diets.*
Special Activities: *Retreats tend to operate as courses unless a private retreat is specified. Day events are open to non-residents.*
Situation: *Quiet suburb.*
Maximum Stay: *30 days.*
Bookings: *By letter or telephone.*
Charges: *£17 per person per day. Concessions if you are poor.*
Access: *By rail or car to Edinburgh. Local buses: from Waverley station.*

God in his mercy looks on you not for what you are, nor for what you have been, but for what you wish to be. - The Cloud of Unknowing

St Peter's Pastoral & Retreat Centre 33 Briar Road
Newlands
Glasgow G24 2TU   Telephone: 041-633 0484

Roman Catholic – Ecumenical

Glorious Glasgow, with its clean streets and polite young people,
boasts the magnificent Burrell Art Collection, theatres and garden
festivals that are all on your doorstep if you stay here – and St Peter's
is happy for you to use its facilities for either a retreat or a holiday
break.

Open: *All year except Christmas and New Year and 3 weeks in July/*
August. Receives men, women, young people, families, groups and
non-retreatants.
Rooms: *34 singles, 8 doubles.*
Facilities: *Disabled, conferences, garden, guest lounge, TV and pay*
phone. Children welcomed.
Spiritual Help: *Only as arranged by retreatants themselves.*
Guests Admitted to: *Chapel, small oratory.*
Meals: *Everyone eats together. Traditional varied menu, with provi-*
sion for vegetarian and special diets.
Special Activities: *Planned programme of events. Send for bro-*
chure.
Situation: *Quiet, extensive grounds – lovely for short walks or a*
quiet time. 15 minutes' drive from city centre.
Maximum Stay: *1 week.*
Bookings: *By telephone – confirm by letter.*
Charges: *Send for the separate tariff.*
Access: *By rail, bus or car to Glasgow.*

GRAMPIAN

Aberdeen

St Margaret's Convent
17 Spital
Aberdeen AB2 3HT   Telephone: 0224 632648

Scottish Episcopal (Anglican)

Open: *All year round except short periods spring and autumn.*
Receives men, women, young people and non-retreatants.

Rooms: *2 singles, 2 doubles.*
Facilities: *Small garden, small library, guest lounge and TV. Children by special arrangement.*
Spiritual Help: *Personal talks, directed study when Chaplain available.*
Guests Admitted to: *Chapel, choir.*
Meals: *Everyone eats together. Very plain food with provision for vegetarian and special diets.*
Special Activities: *No planned programme of events.*
Situation: *Rather busy, in the city. The convent is situated on a high ridge above the road and can be reached only by a steep path and steps.*
Maximum Stay: *2 weeks.*
Bookings: *By letter.*
Charges: *Realistic donation.*
Access: *BR: Aberdeen, then taxi. Car: Aberdeen.*

Elgin

Pluscarden Abbey
Elgin
Moray IV30 3UA   Telephone: 034 389 257
                                      (no calls after 7.30 p.m.)
Roman Catholic

Pluscarden Abbey is at the foot of a steep hill, surrounded by dense, Caledonian-pine forest and pastureland. It is remote and very beautiful here. The vale of St Anres is quite the most extraordinarily magnificent glen to be found in northern Scotland's farmland. Roedeer proliferate, along with buzzards and red squirrels, while Highland cattle roam in the forests. The Abbey is a 13th-century Benedictine monastery, repopulated in 1948 by the Benedictines, who are restoring it. Notable is the stained glass designed by the monks – to my mind one of the few successful marriages of modern and medieval aesthetics. The monastery counts about 30 monks – now famous for their Latin plain-chant Masses, which have been recorded for distribution on both sides of the Atlantic. The Benedictine tradition of hospitality is well observed. Guests may attend all worship, but a rule of silence has to be respected. However, the Guestmaster is happy to converse and may invite you to join in the work – mainly gardening, log-cutting or assistance in the kitchen. Guest facilities are strictly limited.

Open: *All year except over Christmas. Receives men, women, families, groups, religious and non-retreatants.*
Rooms: *7 singles for men, 10 for women only, 2 doubles for women.*
Facilities: *Garden, library with permission, guest lounge and pay phone. Not suitable for the disabled,*
Spiritual Help: *Personal talks, worship and prayer, Divine Office. People in need may ask for guidance from the Guestmaster or Abbot.*
Guests Admitted to: *Chapel, choir and men may share in some work of the community .*
Meals: *Meals for men in refectory; DIY for women in guest house. Very plain food, mainly vegetarian, almost all produced by the monks themselves.*
Special Activities: *No planned programme of events.*
Situation: *Very quiet, in the Vale of St Andrews.*
Maximum Stay: *2 weeks.*
Bookings: *By letter.*
Charges: *By donation, according to your means.*
Access: *BR: to Elgin. Bus: runs on school days. Car: direct route from Elgin, about 6 miles away.*

Findhorn

Minton House
Findhorn
Moray IV36 0TZ   Telephone: 0309 690819

Non-religious - New Age

While following the general philosophy of the Findhorn Foundation (see next entry), this is a separate organisation and more of a retreat centre. The purpose of the Minton Trust which runs the place is to seek through direct experience a deepening of spiritual awareness and to encourage a renewal of Christian worship. Guests are able to share in some of the Findhorn events and facilities.The house is a large pink mansion standing on the shoreline of Findhorn Bay and set in seven acres with lovely views.

Open: *All year. Receives men, women, young people, families in summer season, groups and non-retreatants.*
Rooms: *3 singles, 4 doubles, family room for 4.*
Facilities: *Disabled, sanctuary room, meditation room, conferences, garden, library, guest lounge and pay phone. Children welcomed in summer season.*

Spiritual Help: *Personal talks, group sharing, meditation, and complementary therapies such as massage by arrangement. Weekly worship services using the Taize (see entry under France) chants.*
Guests Admitted to: *Almost everywhere, Shrine room, work of community.*
Meals: *Everyone eats together. Wholefood with provision for vegetarians and special diets.*
Special Activities: *Planned programme of events. Send for brochure. Also concerts, dances, theatre and recitals.*
Situation: *On the shores of Findhorn Bay, lovely landscape.*
Maximum Stay: *1 month.*
Bookings: *By letter or telephone.*
Charges: *Available on application.*
Access: *BR: to Forres, then by taxi. Bus: from Inverness to Forres, then Findhorn. Easy by car.*

Forres

The Findhorn Foundation
The Park, Forres
Morayshire IV36 OTZ   Telephone: 0309 690311

New Age

The Community or Foundation was founded in 1962 with one family living in a caravan. Nature spirits, or 'devas', are said to have allowed them to raise vegetables and exotic flowers from a barren soil of sand and gravel. A permanent community of 150–200 now lives near the gardens, next to which an area of wilderness has been left for the 'devas' – out of bounds to humans. Enthusiasm, harmony and love are the precepts by which the Community works, and there is a strong emphasis on meditation. Hard work is demanded from all paying guests, including those attending courses. Courses of all descriptions run throughout the year. The idea behind this is to create a 'spiritual school', led by 'focalisers' who teach anything from T'ai Ch'i to ecology. Art, graphic design and 'sacred dance' are also popular pursuits here. Such is the popularity of Findhorn among New Age spirituality followers that it is hard to get accommodation unless you book months in advance. The place is generally quite crowded. Indeed, about 5,000 people visit Findhorn annually. Findhorn is not for the poor. Actual retreats are run in a secondary centre in Iona (not part of the 'Iona Community', which is a separate organisation). They cost £95 per week and run from 14 July to 8 September. Before booking the retreat, you must complete an 'experience week' or 'living the life we choose' course (costing £180–£240). Another island retreat on Erraid, near Iona, is available on the same terms. Findhorn is not a place for a private retreat as understood in the Christian or Buddhist traditions.

Open: *All year. Receives men, women, young people, groups, families and non-retreatants.*

Rooms: *Camping, 16 caravans, 90 bed spaces.*

Facilities: *Disabled, sanctuary, conferences, garden, park, library, guest lounge, TV and pay phone. Children welcomed if supervised.*

Spiritual Help: *Personal talks, group sharing, meditation, directed study.*

Guests Admitted to: *Unrestricted access except to private houses and rooms for course study.*

Meals: *Everyone eats together. Traditional food, with provision for vegetarians. Self-catering in caravans.*

Special Activities: *Planned programme of events – send for the brochure. Spontaneous folk-music entertainment in evenings.*

Situation: *Quiet, but crowded in summer. Near village, on estuary peninsula, miles of sand-dune walking. RAF base next door – can be noisy.*

Maximum Stay: *3 months.*

Bookings: *By letter or telephone.*

Charges: *Send for details.*

Access: *By rail to Inverness, then to Forres. Car route easy.*

HIGHLAND

Beauly

Centre of Light
Tigh Na Bruaich
Struy by Beauly
Inverness IV4 7JU

Telephone: 046 376 254

Non-religious

This is a centre for alternative healing set in the Highlands and run by a therapist in natural healing. Her approach to individual well-being is fourfold: concern for spirituality, chemical make-up (including food intake), the body and the emotions. The centre serves as a base for other practitioners who offer various courses. Situated in the

Highlands in a beautiful glen, there are mountains all around, rivers, trees and even a waterfalls.**Highly Recommended.**

Open: *All year. Receives men, women, young people, families and groups.*
Rooms: *1 single, 1 double. Cottage for up to 10 people.*
Facilities: *Garden, telephone.*
Spiritual Help: *Personal talks, group sharing, meditation, and directed study. Spiritual guidence, healing and therapy including kinesiology, rebirthing, Reiki, visualisation and colour work.*
Guests Admitted to: *Unrestricted access, also access with permission to a Highland estate.*
Meals: *Everyone eats together. Wholefood vegetarian.*
Special Activities: *Courses exploring the self through nature and spirit - individual daily sessions for a week or longer. Send for brochure.*
Situation: *Very quiet and situated in a beautiful wooded glen in grounds of 5 acres.*
Maximum Stay: *2 weeks.*
Bookings: *By letter or telephone.*
Charges: *£425 per person per week, £70 per day, £375 per week per person for a group retreat.*
Access: *BR: to Inverness – they will collect you.*

Fort Augustus

St Benedict's Abbey
Fort Augustus
Inverness-shire PH32 4DB   Telephone: 0320 6232

Roman Catholic

The buildings are rather heavy Victorian Gothic and less attractive than one might expect. However, there are some interesting features – a Roman plaque, Loch Ness, and a dungeon, now an underground chapel. School playing-fields and a garden surround the Abbey. Despite the size of the building (which covers about 15 acres), only about 30 monks inhabit the place. It is in a beautiful state of repair and upkeep, but one gets the impression that this is a dwindling institution. Because of its location on the tourist route of the Great Glen, the Abbey is always stretched to provide guest accommodation. Those wishing for a retreat in this busy centre should visit in the winter months only, which is during the school term so expect some degree of noise. The monks are cultured, courteous and excellent conversationalists. The prospective retreatant would be well advised to visit the monastery a few times to get to know some of the monks before staying with them, otherwise one might miss the understated but very deep warmth of the brethren.

Open: *All year. Receives men, women, young people, and groups.*
Rooms: *Single men in the monastery. Groups in lodge guest house.*
Facilities: *Chapel, garden, library, guest lounge and pay phone.*
Spiritual Help: *Personal talks. Sacrament of Reconciliation daily, Mass.*
Guests Admitted to: *Chapel, choir and work of the community.*
Meals: *Everyone eats together or in the refectory.. Traditional food.*
Special Activities: *No planned programme of events.*
Situation: *Quiet, in the town. Stunning views of Loch Ness and Monadhliath Mountains.*
Maximum Stay: *By arrangement.*
Bookings: *By letter.*
Charges: *By arrangement - but basic of £10 B&B plus £5 per day for meals.*
Access: *Easy access by bus. BR: Spean Bridge or Inverness.*

Garve

Samadhan Workshop Centre
Scoraig Peninsula
Dundonnell
by Garve
Wester Ross IV23 2RE   Telephone: 085 483 260

New Age – Non-denominational

The word 'samadhan' means 'the answer', and the founder of this private centre is Sundara Forsyth, a Shiatsu practitioner. She holds voice healing workshops throughout the year. Visitors can expect a long journey no matter how they travel, but the rewards are many – not least the peace and quiet of a remote coastland and the wildlife that abounds there, including a large herd of rare indigenous mountain goats. The centre contains a light, modern room for meditation and courses. Bedrooms are comfortable and every bed has a thick duvet. In addition to Shiatsu, individual instruction in voice healing, rebirthing and movement ritual are offered.
Open: *All year. Receives men, women, young people, groups and*

non-retreatants.
Rooms: *5 singles, 3 doubles.*
Facilities: *Small conferences, camping, garden, library, guest lounge,
TV and guest telephone. No children or pets.*
Spiritual Help: *Personal talks, some counselling, group sharing,
meditation.*
Guests Admitted to: *Unrestricted access, work of household.*
Meals: *Everyone eats together. Wholefood is provided which is
almost always vegetarian but sometimes fish is served.*
Special Activities: *Planned programme. Send for brochure.*
Situation: *Wilderness – remote, beautiful and peaceful. Walking,
boating and fishing available.*
Maximum Stay: *By arrangement.*
Bookings: *By letter or telephone.*
Charges: *Ask for rates for individual instruction and workshops.*
Access: *70 miles from Inverness to Badluarach, where you leave the
car. Boatman will ferry you to Samadhan. Westerbus on Monday,
Wednesday, Saturday to Badcaul, where you will be met. Via post-
boat or on foot from Badrallagh.*

LOTHIAN

Haddington

Sancta Maria Abbey
Nunraw Guest House
Haddington
East Lothian EH41 4LW   Telephone: 062 083 223

Roman Catholic

More people want to stay at this Cistercian monastery and guest house
than can be accommodated, so don't be disappointed if it is full. The
surrounding countryside is very beautiful and the monastery runs a
large agricultural establishment. This is a place of silence and deep
spirituality, where you may truly put aside the burdens of everyday
living and open yourself to the benefits of silence and solitude.

Open: *All year except Christmas and November. Receives men,
women, young people, and groups up to 20.*
Rooms: *Accommodation for 30 in single, double, and dormitory
rooms in the guest house.*
Facilities: *Park, library, guest lounge and direct-dialling pay phone.*

Children welcomed.
Spiritual Help: *Personal talks.*
Guests Admitted to: *Chapel.*
Meals: *Traditional food taken in the guest house.*
Special Activities: *No planned programme of events.*
Situation: *Very quiet and in the countryside.*
Maximum Stay: *By arrangement.*
Bookings: *By letter.*
Charges: *According to means.*
Access: *By car.*

---

*' Prayer is an encounter and a relationship, a relationship which
is deep, and this relationship cannot be forced either on us or on
God' – Metropolitan Anthony of Sourozh*

Musselburgh

Carberry Tower
Musselburgh
Midlothian EH21 8PY   Telephone: 031-665 3135

Church of Scotland

Carberry Tower is a very Scottish country-house with delightful
public rooms and a good library. The programme is extensive and
includes youth weekends, open and midweek courses, and Bible
study.

Open: *All year. Receives men, women, young people, families and
children, groups, religious and non-retreatants.*
Rooms: *20 singles, 30 doubles, plus dormitories.*
Facilities: *Conferences, camping, garden, park, library, guest
lounge, TV and pay phone. Children welcomed.*
Spiritual Help: *Groups participate in a scheduled programme, or
they arrange their own. No direction for individuals.*
Guests Admitted to: *Unrestricted access.*
Meals: *Everyone eats together. Traditional food, with provision for
vegetarian and special diets.*
Special Activities: *Lots of activities, including courses almost every
weekend. Send for brochure.*
Situation: *Very quiet but busy because of guests. Set in 30 acres of*

parkland with fine trees.
Maximum Stay: *By arrangement.*
Bookings: *Telephone first but confirm by letter.*
Charges: *From £15 to £31 per day.*
Access: *See good map and directions in brochure.*

STRATHCLYDE

Isle of Cumbrae

The College
Millport
Isle of Cumbrae KA28 OHE　　　　Telephone: 0475 530353

Anglican

Open: *All year – closed December and January. Receives men, women, groups and non-retreatants.*
Rooms: *9 singles, 5 doubles, 6 twin-bedded rooms.*
Facilities: *Conferences, garden, library, guest lounge and payphone.*
Spiritual Help: *None, but the College is attached to the Cathedral for worship.*
Guests Admitted to: *Chapel.*
Meals: *Everyone eats together – the food is traditional.*
Special Activities: *No planned programme of events.*
Situation: *Very quiet.*
Maximum Stay: *By arrangement.*
Bookings: *By letter.*
Charges: *£14 B&B, £21 B&B plus evening meal.*
Access: *By rail plus Ferry.*

'There is no thought, feeling or desire within us which cannot become the substance of prayer' – Gerald W. Hughes

Isle of Iona

The Iona Community
The Abbey & The MacLeod Centre
Isle of Iona
Argyll PA76 6SN   Telephone: 06817 404

Christian – Ecumenical

The Iona Community is an ecumenical movement of ordained and lay Christians and welcomes more than 150,000 visitors to this ancient, holy island every year. It was on Iona that St Columba in 563 AD began his mission to bring Christianity to Scotland. The 13th-century Benedictine abbey and church have now been restored. There is an extensive programme of courses and events but retreats are possible in November.

Open: *Open March to December. Receives men, women, young people, families and groups.*
Rooms: *3 single, 13 double and a dormitory.*
Facilities: *Disabled in the MacLeod Centre, garden, common room and pay phone. Children welcome. This is not a conference centre nor a " quiet house."*
Spiritual Help: *Guests are expected to join in the community life.*
Guests Admitted to: *Unrestricted.*
Meals: *Everyone eats together. Food is mainly vegetarian with three meat meals a week.*
Special Activities: *Guests share chores, join in worship, concerts, workshops, discussions, and study.*
Situation: *Quiet, near village, set on an island in Inner Hebrides.*
Maximum Stay: *Usually 1 week.*
Bookings: *Send for booking form.*
Charges: *About £151 per person per week.*
Access: *Train from Glasgow to Oban, then ferry to Isle of Mull, bus or car 37 miles across Mull, finally a ferry to Iona.*

'God is beauty' – St Francis of Assisi

Isle of Iona

Bishop's House
Isle of Iona
Argyll PA76 6SJ   Telephone: 06817 306

Scottish Episcopal Church

Devoid of many of the distractions of the 20th century, Iona is a good place to rediscover simplicity and to feel some unity with nature and creation. It has been steeped in Christian prayer for 14 centuries. Bishop's House is both a place for retreat and for those who may wish to take a very quiet break in a Christian environment. There is a resident chaplain and the house runs 'open week' retreats for those coming as individuals. The house with its many gables and rose window above the entrance is appealing in its rather stark setting.

Open: *March to October. Receives men, women, young people, families, groups, non-retreatants.*
Rooms: *3 singles, 3 doubles, 7 twin-bedded rooms.*
Facilities: *Garden, library, guest lounge and pay phone.*
Spiritual Help: *Personal talks.*
Guests Admitted to: *Unrestricted access everywhere.*
Meals: *Everyone eats together. Good, varied home-cooking, with provision for vegetarian and special diets.*
Special Activities: *Most guests come in parish parties and often bring their own chaplain and organise their own programme, but individuals are welcomed too.*
Situation: *Very quiet in remote, romantic setting.*
Maximum Stay: *2 weeks.*
Bookings: *By letter or telephone.*
Charges: *£24.50 per person full board, £13.50 B&B. See brochure for other rates.*
Access: *No easy way. (See entry for Iona Community)*

'Prayer has been man's unceasing cry to God.
It is the most universal evidence that there is in him something
higher than his natural life' – Abbot Vonier

Isle of Skye

Quiraing Lodge
Staffin
Isle of Skye IV51 9JS   Telephone: 047 062330

New Age

The house is surrounded by an acre of garden, sloping down to the shore while behind rise the magnificent hills of the Quiraing. Good walks all around, with bicycles available for those who want to explore further afield. The programme is varied with an interest in deepening relationships with Gaia and the spiritual forces in nature.

Open: *All year. Receives men, women, groups, non-retreatants.*
Rooms: *4 three-bedded rooms and 3 with twin beds.*
Facilities: *Guest lounge, dining room, library, music area, healing room, sanctuary. No smoking.*
Spiritual Help: *Group sharing, yoga.*
Guests Admitted to: *Access everywhere.*
Meals: *Everyone eats together. Vegetarian home-cooked food with organic produce where possible. Special diets on request.*
Special Activities: *Yoga holidays, weaving and spinning summer school, watercolour painting, special Gaia courses. Send for brochure.*
Situation: *Peaceful in the middle of hills, mountains, countryside.*
Maximum Stay: *By arrangement.*
Bookings: *By letter or telephone.*
Charges: *B&B £14, full board £24 per day.*
Access: *Coach, rail, car and air are all possible, so ask for details.*

Largs

Benedictine Monastery
5 Mackerston Place
Largs
Ayrshire KA30 8BY   Telephone: 0475 687320

Roman Catholic

A quiet and comfortable place where you will be left to structure your own day or follow the prayer rhythm of the nuns. With no organised retreats or programmes, this is a retreat house designed for the world-weary whose spiritual energies are at a low ebb.

Open: *All year except Christmas. Receives men, women, young people, groups, non-retreatants.*
Rooms: *10 singles,1 double.*
Facilities: *Library, chapel, guest lounge, small garden.*
Spiritual Help: *Divine Office, Mass, personal talks.*
Guests Admitted to: *Chapel.*
Meals: *DIY for breakfast. Lunch and supper served. Traditional food. Vegetarian food can be arranged if absolutely necesssary. No special diets.*
Special Activities: *None.*
Situation: *Quiet.*
Maximum Stay: *2 weeks.*
Bookings: *By letter.*
Charges: *£15 per person per day.*
Access: *BR: to Largs from Glasgow. Car: follow Clyde coastal route from Glasgow.*

Mull

Camas Centre
Island of Mull
Mull, Argyll
Strathclyde   Telephone: 06817 4404

Christian - Ecumenical

Young people and children, especially from urban areas, often need the spiritual refreshment of their own retreat. Few are available, but here is one which takes 16 young guests with a caring staff who all get acquainted through sharing together worship, work, and outdoor activities. The Centre is a stone-built salmon fishing station about three miles from Iona and a short walk over a moor. Walking, abseiling, canoeing and even the excitement of a night spent sleeping in a cave are on offer. Camas weeks run from June to September and the cost including rail fare ranges from £86.35 to £21.00 depending on age and means. Other charges are available for accommodation only and for shorter stays. The Centre is run by and from the MacLeod Centre on Iona (see entry).

Crieff

St Ninian's Centre
Comrie Road
Crieff
Perthshire PH7 4BG   Telephone: 0764 653766

Interdenominational

A former church, St Ninian's, has been adapted into a modern residential centre, providing a wide range of courses, retreats, renewal weekends and refreshment breaks. The little town of Crieff is situated in pretty countryside and has much to offer in the way of parks and nature trails for walking, and local sports facilities, including fishing.

Open: *All year except Christmas. Receives men, women, young people, families and groups.*
Rooms: *22 singles, 14 doubles, dormitory.*
Facilities: *Conferences, library, guest lounge, TV and guest pay phone. Children welcomed, guide dogs permitted.*
Spiritual Help: *Group sharing and directed study. Staff assist at mission-training and renewal conferences held for elders, lay preachers, church groups and youth groups.*
Guests Admitted to: *Chapel.*
Meals: *Everyone eats together. Traditional food, with provision for vegetarian and special diets.*
Special Activities: *Planned programme of events. Send for brochure.*
Situation: *In the town, near countryside and with good views. Central for shops and park.*
Maximum Stay: *By arrangement.*
Bookings: *By letter.*
Charges: *Send for tariff.*
Access: *By rail, bus or car via Perth and Stirling.*

Fife

Tabor Retreat Centre
Key House
High Street
Falkland, Fife   Telephone: 0337 857705

Ecumenical

An ordinary old 18th century Scottish house in a beautiful setting with a warm, relaxed and informal atmosphere. Situated next door to Falkland Palace, used by the Kings of Scotland, the house overlooks the Palace orchard. In many Protestant circles, the idea of going on a traditional retreat is a new concept - one long put aside following the Reformation. Tabor Retreat Centre offers a 'taster' stay to encourage and acquaint such people with the idea of retreat. The Centre is run by a deaconess and the morning and evening worship is based on Iona Community liturgies.

Open: *Tuesdays to Sundays all year. Receives men, women, young people, and groups.*
Rooms: *4 singles, 8 doubles.*
Facilities: *Day retreats, garden, and guest phone.*
Spiritual Help: *Personal talks, meditation, and directed study.*
Guests Admitted to: *Access to most areas, including chapel.*
Meals: *Everyone eats together. Wholefood with provision for vegetarians and special diets.*
Special Activities: *Planned events. Send for brochure.*
Situation: *Quiet in a village.*
Maximum Stay: *5 nights.*
Bookings: *By letter or telephone.*
Charges: *Suggested offering is £22.50 per 24 hrs, but subsidised if necessary according to means.*
Access: *BR to Markinch. Bus: Glenrothes, then local bus. Car: 5 miles from M90.*

Perth

St Mary's Mission & Renewal Centre
St Mary's Monastery
Kinnoull
Perth PH2 7BP   Telephone: 0738 24075

Roman Catholic

This is a large, rather institutional retreat centre overlooking Perth and enjoying peaceful seclusion. There is plenty of accommodation here, and retreat and renewal courses (one lasting six weeks) are available for both lay guests and religious. Individuals are welcome throughout the year.

Open: *All year. Receives men, women, religious and groups.*

Rooms: *16 singles, 21 doubles.*

Facilities: *Conferences, garden, library, guest lounge, TV and guest pay phone (0738 36487).*

Spiritual Help: *Personal talks, group sharing, and special renewal courses.*

Guests Admitted to: *Access to most areas, including chapel.*

Meals: *Everyone eats together. Traditional food, with provision for vegetarians and special diets.*

Special Activities: *Planned events and courses. Send for brochure.*

Situation: *Quiet, above the city.*

Maximum Stay: *By arrangement.*

Bookings: *By letter or telephone.*

Charges: *Enquire when requesting brochure or booking to stay.*

Access: *BR to Perth, bus thereafter. By car to Perth city, then via Hatton Road to St Mary's Monastery.*

Northern Ireland

Belfast

Columbanus Community of Reconciliation
683 Antrim Road
Belfast BT15 4EG   Telephone: 0232 778009

Most of the guests at Columbanus are interested in the religious and socio-political situation in Northern Ireland. They use this place as a base from which to explore such implications and as a means of informing themselves on a personal basis. Using this experience they hope to create change in their own cultural and church environments. Programmes can be arranged for groups. This is very much an ecumenical community, comprising Roman Catholic, Anglican and Presbyterian members, all of whom share the aims and ministry of reconciliation.

Open: *All year except for 3 weeks in August. Receives men, women, young people, groups and non-retreatants.*
Rooms: *1 single, 2 doubles, dormitories.*
Facilities: *Door ramps for the disabled but no sleeping facilities. Small conferences, large garden, nearby park, library, guest lounge, TV and direct-dialling telephone.*
Spiritual Help: *Community prayers – morning and evening and for anyone around at lunch-time. Spiritual direction can sometimes be offered to individuals.*
Guests Admitted to: *Unrestricted access for individuals.*
Meals: *Eaten together in dining room. Tasty, wholesome food, with provision for vegetarians. Self-catering for groups.*
Special Activities: *Occasional lectures – faith, history, ecumenics.*
Situation: *In the city, rather busy.*
Maximum Stay: *Unlimited.*
Bookings: *By letter.*
Charges: *Sample rates: £15 per person, full board; £8 B&B; £3 lunch; £4 dinner.*
Access: *Buses: Nos. 1, 2, 3, 4, 5, 6, 45 from City Hall.*

Republic of Ireland

Beara

Dzogchen Beara
Garranes Allihies
West Cork   Telephone: 027 730 32

Buddhist – Tibetan

This is a meditation and retreat centre for Buddhist study and practice.
It is 400 feet up on the cliffs above Bantry Bay, with a vast panorama
of the Atlantic Ocean. Guests stay in self-catering houses and studios.
Dzogchen Beara is under the spiritual direction of Sogyal Rinpoche,
a lama, scholar and meditation master. Born in Tibet, he has been
living in the West for many years.

Open: *All year. Receives men, women, young people, families,
groups and non-retreatants.*
Rooms: *Singles and doubles available in 5 separate holiday-houses
as well as an independent hostel.*
Facilities: *Conferences, garden, meditation prayer room, pay phone.
Children welcomed.*
Spiritual Help: *Meditation, personal talks.*
Guests Admitted to: *Shrine room.*
Meals: *Self-catering.*
Special Activities: *Programme of planned events – send for
brochure. Near famous gardens. Good walking with sporting
facilities in vicinity, offering tennis, riding, sailing, fishing and golf.*
Situation: *Very quiet, in countryside.*
Maximum Stay: *By arrangement.*
Bookings: *By telephone or letter.*
Charges: *From £100 to £235 per week for holiday-houses. Other
charges per person on request.*
Access: *By bus or car from Cork.*

Cobh

St Benedict's Priory
The Mount
Cobh
Cork   Telephone: 021 811354

Roman Catholic

This Community moved to Ireland from Sussex and now continues to offer silence, space and rest to their guests.

Open: *All year. Receives men, women, young people and small groups.*
Rooms: *6 singles, 2 doubles.*
Facilities: *Garden, library, guest lounge, and guest telephone. No rooms on ground floor.*
Spiritual Help: *Personal talks if required. Share in the liturgy of the Community.*
Guests Admitted to: *Chapel.*
Meals: *Lunch provided, DIY facilities for other meals. Traditional food, with provision for vegetarians.*
Special Activities: *Rest and quiet. A programme including Irish monasticism incorporating local history is being planned so write during the year to find out what might be on offer. Enclose a SAE please.*
Situation: *Quiet, in a picturesque town on an island in Cork harbour, so the sea is at hand. Beautiful countryside a few minutes away.*
Maximum Stay: *1 week.*
Bookings: *By letter or telephone.*
Charges: *Donation, but about £15 IR per person covers daily costs.*
Access: *Train, road or ferry to Cobh.*

Montenotte (Cork)

St Dominic's Priory and Retreat Centre
Ennismore
Montenotte
Cork   Telephone: 021 502520

Roman Catholic

'Get up and make your way to the potter's house: there I shall let you hear what I have to say' (Jeremiah 18:2). This is a good line of Scripture to bear in mind, if you find a weekend course entitled 'pottery meditations' too curious. Other stimulating courses on offer here from the resident Dominican community include charismatic retreats for lay guests and religious, retreats for retired lay people, and reflexology and meditation workshops.

Open: *All year except 24 December to 6 January. Receives men, women, young people, groups and non-retreatants.*

Rooms: *40 singles, 6 doubles, dormitories for 50, hermitage, barn.*
Facilities: *Limited for disabled, conferences, garden, park, library, guest lounge and direct-dialling pay phone.*
Spiritual Help: *Personal talks, group sharing, meditation and directed study.*
Guests Admitted to: *Almost unrestricted access to all areas, including chapel, choir, shrine room, some work of the community.*
Meals: *Taken in the guest house. Traditional food, with provision for vegetarian and special diets. Self-catering facilities available.*
Special Activities: *Planned programme of events. Send for brochure.*
Situation: *Quiet, in the countryside, but can be rather busy. With 30 acres of grounds and spectacularly situated gardens, the Centre feels as though it is in open countryside, but is only 3 miles from the city centre.*
Maximum Stay: *Unlimited.*
Bookings: *By telephone but confirmation by letter required.*
Charges: *Various rates, so send for details.*
Access: *By rail to Cork. Bus: No. 8 from city centre. Car: see map in brochure.*

DUBLIN

Dublin

Dominican Retreat & Pastoral Centre
Tallaght
Dublin 24
Telephone: Dublin 515002

Roman Catholic

There are good facilities here for the disabled, as well as accommodation with DIY cooking facilities for those wishing to make a silent retreat in the 'poustinia' tradition. Although in the town, it is quiet and there is a garden and park.

Open: *All year except Christmas and September. Receives men, women, young people, and groups.*
Rooms: *35 singles, 5 doubles, hermitage.*
Facilities: *Conferences, chapel, garden, and pay phone.*
Spiritual Help: *Personal talks and meditation.*
Guests Admitted to: *Unrestricted access.*
Meals: *Everyone eats together. Traditional food with provision for*

special diets.
Special Activities: *Planned programme of events. Send for brochure.*
Situation: *In town, but quiet.*
Maximum Stay: *1 week.*
Bookings: *By letter or telephone.*
Charges: *£23 IR per person per day, full board.*
Access: *Bus: No. 77 or 77a from centre of Dublin.*

KERRY

Ardfert

Ardfert Retreat Centre
Ardfert
County Kerry   Telephone: 066 34276

Roman Catholic

The Centre is staffed by Presentation Sisters and a priest director, and serves some 54 parishes. While this is a place for group bookings, individuals wishing to join any Saturday or Sunday parish-group retreat are welcome to do so by prior arrangement with the secretary of the Centre. There is a new lending-library service for books and videos on Christian topics.

Open: *Most of the year, but check, as they are closed for four weeks in summer. Receives men, women, young people, and groups.*
Rooms: *30 singles.*
Facilities: *A diocesan retreat centre in constant use by parish groups and schools.*
Guests Admitted to: *Almost unrestricted access.*
Spiritual Help: *Personal talks, spiritual direction, group sharing and meditation.*
Meals: *Available for groups but not for individual visitors. Traditional food.*
Special Activities: *These range from residential weekends of prayer and Ennegram workshops to days of support and prayer for dependants of those suffering from alcoholism. Send for brochure.*
Situation: *Very quiet, in the countryside.*
Maximum Stay: *According to the programme.*
Bookings: *By letter.*
Charges: *Offering of £36 per person or £60 per couple. Preached*

retreats: £19 per day, and directed retreats: £21 per day.
Access: *Train and bus to Tralee. Car: Centre is 5 miles north of Tralee.*

Murroe

Glenstal Abbey
Murroe
County Limerick   Telephone: 061 386103

Roman Catholic

Glenstal, founded in 1927 on the site of a medieval abbey, has a tradition of involvement in arts and crafts, in the areas of sculpture, metalwork, wood-turning and pottery, and runs a nearby school. This is a large and active community, perhaps one of the very few that can say that guests may be admitted to the choir 'if room is available'. In most monasteries today there are more empty choir-stalls than filled ones at Divine Office. In 1975, the Abbey founded a new monastic community in Nigeria and these links with Africa have been strengthened over the years.

Open: *All year except Christmas. Receives men, women, young people and sometimes non-retreatants.*
Rooms: *8 singles, 2 doubles.*
Facilities: *Conferences by arrangement, park and gardens, small library and pay phone.*
Spiritual Help: *Personal talks if requested.*
Guests Admitted to: *Chapel and choir, if room is available.*
Meals: *Some meals taken with monastic community, others in the parlour. Traditional food; arrangements can be made for vegetarian or special diets. Tea- and coffee-making facilities.*
Special Activities: *No planned programme of events.*
Situation: *Very quiet and in the countryside.*
Maximum Stay: *By arrangement.*
Bookings: *By letter.*
Charges: *On application..*
Access: *Rail from Dublin, buses infrequent. Car: Abbey is 12 miles from Limerick, off the Dublin Road.*

'If a care is too small to be turned into a prayer, it is too small to be made into a burden' – Corrie ten Boom

Roscrea

Mount St Joseph Abbey
Roscrea
County Tipperary   Telephone: 0505 21711

Roman Catholic – Ecumenical

Almost 300 boys attend secondary school here, and this active and large community of Cistercian monks have made no less than three new foundations since the war – one each in Ireland, Scotland and Australia. The Abbey is set in quiet countryside and the atmosphere is conducive to prayer and relaxation. The monastic choir and liturgy is deeply rich and inspiring.

Open: *All year except Christmas. Receives men, women, young people individually, groups and non-retreatants.*
Rooms: *12 singles, 5 doubles, 7 twin-bedded rooms.*
Facilities: *Conferences, limited library, guest lounge and pay phone.*
Spiritual Help: *Personal talks, meditation can be made privately in prayer room in the guest house or in the church.*
Guests Admitted to: *Chapel.*
Meals: *Everyone eats together in the guest house – traditional food.*
Special Activities: *No planned programme of events.*
Situation: *In quiet countryside.*
Maximum Stay: *2 weeks.*
Bookings: *By letter or telephone.*
Charges: *On application.*
Access: *By rail or car from Dublin. Bus: to Roscrea town – guest house 3 miles away.*

'It is rare to find anyone who is truly reasonable, for we are usually diverted from the path of reason by self-love' – St Francis de Sales

Yoga Centres

There are many local yoga classes as well as clubs and groups throughout Britain and across Europe. Most of these do not own a meeting centre of their own, so they meet in various venues, from halls to community and local leisure centres. In many cases the area or regional organisation is run by a volunteer and all correspondence is carried out from home. Educational authorities are increasingly including yoga classes in their adult education programmes. Most of the yoga teachers' associations will provide you with a list of the teachers, courses and classes in your area. The following two national organisations are information centres for yoga in Britain and can help you to locate a yoga centre or class, if none of the ones listed here is convenient.

British Wheel of Yoga
1 Hamilton Place
Boston Road
Sleaford, Lincs. NG34 7ES   Telephone: 0529 306851

Founded in 1965 and affiliated to the European Union of Federations of Yoga, the Wheel has a nationwide network of teachers and representatives who are available to help you at a local level. Good information is available on yoga practices and they can usually provide a list of teachers in your immediate area.

Open Centres
Avrils Farm
Lower Stanton St. Quintin
Chippenham
Wiltshire SN14 6PA   Telephone: 0249 720202

Open Centres publishes an excellent bi-annual non-profit-making newsletter which links various yoga centres, groups, private houses and people who share the aim of being open to the truth through meditation, movement, healing and interfaith work. As well as a directory, the newsletter contains varied and interesting articles.

London
Beaumont Hall Yoga Centre, Contact: Peter Ballard, 2 Beaumont Grove, Stepney, E1, Tel: 081 592 8874.

Satyananda Yoga Centre, 70 Thurleigh Rd., SW12, Tel: 081 673 4869.

Shanti Sadan Centre of Adhyatma Yoga, 29 Chepstow Villas, W11 3DR, Tel: 071 727 7846.

Sivananda Yoga Vendanta Centre, 51 Felsham Rd., SW15 1AZ, Tel: 081 780 0160.

Sunra Yoga & Holistic Health Centre, Contact: Barbara Gordon, 26 Balham Hill, Clapham South, SW12 9EB, Tel: 081 675 9224.

Avon
Viniyoga Britain, Contact: P. Harvey, PO Box 158, Bath, BA1 2YG, Tel: 0225 426327.

Bedfordshire
Yoga for Health Foundation. (See main entry)

Berkshire
Newbury Yoga Circle, Contact: Rose Morris, Whiteways, Thornford Rd., Headley, Nr. Newbury, Tel: 0635 268392.

Buckinghamshire
North Bucks Yoga Teachers' Association, 1 Sir John Pascoe Way, Duston, Northants, NN5 6PN, Tel: 0604 58909.

Cheshire
Cheshire Yoga Teachers' Association, Contact: Miranda Michaelides, 6 Brent Close, Poynton, Tel: 09625 877596.

The Yoga Circle, Contact: M. Priestner, 140 Grove Lane, Hale, Altrincham WA15 8LT, Tel: 061 9040588.

Cleveland
Cleveland Yoga Group, Contact: Mavis Fielding, 3 Recreation View, Moorsholm, TS12 3HZ, Tel: 0642 816055.

Cornwall
Amrit Centre, 24 Tregew Road, Flushing, Falmouth, Cornwall TR11 5TF, Tel: 0326 377529.

Cornwall Yoga Fellowship, Polsue Cottage, Ruan High Lanes, Truro, TR2 5LU, Tel: 0872 501596.

Cumbria
Yoga Quests, Contact: Phillip Xerri, 20 Portland Street, Lancaster LA1 1SZ, Tel: 0524 381154.

Derbyshire
Derbyshire Yoga Teachers' Association, 274 Smedley St., Matlock, DE4. Tel: 0629 56381.

Devon
Devon School of Yoga, 46 St. Paul's Road, Honiton, Devon,
EX14 8BR, Tel: 0404 47346.
Dorset
St. Ronan's House, Contact: M. Tobias, 170 St. Andrew's Rd.,
Bridport DT6 3BW, Tel: 0308 23194.
Durham
Darlington Yoga Group, Contact: Vera Oates, 9 Hillside,
Ingleton, Darlington DL2 3HL, Tel: 0325 730092.
East Sussex
Patanjali Yoga Centre & Ashram, Contact: Sri Indar Nath, The
Cott, Marley Lane, Battle, TN33 ORE, Tel: 0424 870538.
Gloucestershire
Forge House Centre, Forge House, Kemble, GL7 6AD, Tel: 0285
770635.
Greater Manchester
Manchester & District Institute of Iyengar Yoga, 134 King
Street, Dukinfield, Tel: 061 3390748 or 061 3683614.
Hampshire
Sukha Yoga Club, 2 Yew Tree Cottages, Hook Common,
Basingstoke, RG27 9JJ, Tel: 0256 762417.
Karuna Yoga School, Contact: Fiona Ashdown, 28 Arthur Road,
Shirley, Southampton SO1 5DY, Tel: 0703 632881.
Satchidananda Wholistic Trust, Woodside, Sutton Wood Lane,
Bighton, Alresford SO24 9SG, Tel: 0962 773557.
Hertfordshire
Herts Yoga Workshop, Contact: Kerstin Elliot, 28 Marshal's
Drive, St. Albans, AL1 4RQ, Tel: 0727 51547.
Kent
South East Yoga Teachers' Association, 107 Culverden Down,
Tunbridge Wells, TN4 9SN, Tel: 0892 521855.
Leicestershire
Leicestershire Yoga Circle, Contact: Melinda Johnson, 43 Half
Moon Crescent, Oadby, LE2 4DH, Tel: 0533 712520.
Merseyside
Comprehensive Yoga Fellowship, Faith House. (see main entry)
Merseyside Yoga Association, Contact: D. Duckett, 15 Curzon
Road, Waterloo, Liverpool L22 ONL, Tel: 05192 81746.
Norfolk
Norfolk Yoga Group, Contact: Bob Camp, 21 St. Andrew's
Ave.,Thorpe St. Andrew, Norwich NR7 ORG.
Northamptonshire
Body Mind Inc., Mereview, Newtown Road, Raunds, NN9 6LY,
Tel: 0933 623706.

Northamptonshire Yoga Teachers' Association, Contact: Sheila Robinson, 13 Barker Close, Rushden, NN10 OEJ, Tel: 0933 312599.

Northumberland

Northumberland Yoga Group, Contact: Betty Websell, 42 Park Road, Swarland, Felton NE65 9JD, Tel: 0670 787423.

Nottinghamshire

Friends of Yoga Society, Contact: Pauline Mainland, Piriskey, 5 Weston Crescent, Old Sawley, Long Eaton, NG10 3BS.

Oxfordshire

Banbury Yoga Group, Contact: Janice Pearse, 148 Sinclair Ave, Banbury, OX16 7BL, Tel: 0295 262412

Oxford Yoga Group, Contact: Gillian Webster, Shamba, 24 Begbroke Lane, Begbroke, OX5 1RN, Tel: 0865 841018.

Somerset

Self Realization Healing Centre. (See main entry)

Staffordshire

Staffordshire Yoga Fellowship, Contact: Mary Myatt, 78 Church Lane, Hanford, Stoke-on-Trent, ST4 4QD, Tel: 0782 657730.

Surrey

School of Yoga, 22 Old Farleigh Road, Selsdon, Surrey CR2 8PB

Surrey Iyengar Yoga Centre, Church Farm House, Springclose Lane, Cheam, Surrey SM3 8PU, Tel: 081 6440309.

Woking & District Yoga Club, Contact: Ralph Gabriel, Deep Pool, Chobham, near Woking, GU24 8AS, Tel: 0276 858884.

Tyne & Wear

North East Institute of Iyengar Yoga, Contact: Gordon Austin, 8 Staveley Rd., Seaburn Dene, Sunderland, SR6 8JS, Tel: 091 5487457.

West Midlands

Holistic Health Centre, 119 Hagley Road, Stourbridge, DY8 1RD, Tel: 0384 379740.

Birmingham & District Institute of Iyengar Yoga, Contact: Jayne Orton, 66 Bantry Close, Sheldon, Birmingham B26 3LR, Tel: 021 7438143.

Satyananda Yoga Centre, Birmingham, Contact: Ann Fletcher, 38 Gaddesby Road, Kings Heath, Birmingham B14 7EX, Tel: 021 4445976.

Wiltshire

The European Shiatsu School, Central Administration, High Banks, Lockeridge, Marlborough, SN8 4EQ, Tel: 0672 86362.

Yorkshire & Humberside

Holistic Health & Healing Trust, Contact: Constance Cawthorne, 53 Sicey Ave., Sheffield S5 6NL, Tel: 0742 459201.

Charmony Yoga Circle, The Cherries, Rossefield Ave., Birkby, Huddersfield HD2 2BR, Tel: 0484 535298.

NORTHERN IRELAND

Yoga Fellowship of Northern Ireland, 24 Mooreland Park, Belfast BT11 9AZ, Tel: 0232 615085

SCOTLAND

Lendrick Lodge, Brig o.Turk, Trossachs, Perthshire, FK17 8HR, Tel: 08776 263
Scottish Yoga Teachers' Association, Contact: Katy MacFarlane, 19 Norwood Drive, Glasgow G46 78LS, Tel: 042 6381214.
West of Scotland Yoga Teachers' Association, Contact: Pearl Slane, 43a Roman Road, Bearsden, Glasgow G61 2QP, Tel: 041 9430597.

WALES

North Wales Yoga & Natural Therapy Centre, Contact: Helen Humphreys, 2a Erskine Road, Colwyn Bay, Tel: 0492 533961.

IRELAND

Chrysalis, Donoughnmore, Donard, Co. Wicklow, Tel: 045 54713
Meitheal Centre, Inch Island, Co. Donegal.
Macro Health Centre, Trees, Kinnard, W. Kispole, Tralee, Co. Kerry, Tel: 066 51317.

FRANCE

Federation Nationale des Enseignants de Yoga (FNEY), Contact: Ise Masquelier, rue Aubriot 3, F-75004 Paris, Tel: 42 70 03 05
French Yoga-Meditation Retreats, Yewtree Cottage, Spinfield Lane West, Marlow, SL7 2DB.
Inner Garden Yoga Centre, Aelfylon, La Cascade, 30820 Caveirac, Gard.

La Valdieu, Rennes-le-Chateau, 1190 Couiza, Tel: 33 68 74 23 21. Yoga Camp in the summer.
Le Plan, Provence. Contact: L. St. Aubyn, 10 Irene Road, London SW6 4AL.

SPAIN

Asociación Española de Praticantes de Yoga, Marta Pascual, Secretary, Garadener 62 Torre, E-08024, Barcelona, Tel: 3 219 18 41
Galería Art Elemental, C.Merced 33, Facinas 11391, Cadiz, Spain, Tel: 64 5044.

'There is no such thing as " my" bread. All bread is ours *and is given to me, to others through me and to me through others. For not only bread but all things necessary for sustenance in this life are given on loan to us with others, and because of others and for others and to others through us.' - Meister Eckhart*

France

The majority of retreat places in France are Roman Catholic monasteries and convents with a few notable exceptions such as Taizé (see entry), which is a world-famous ecumenical community to which thousands of men and women go each year. While many communities in France have built modern facilities which are often striking in design and concept, most of the monasteries are centuries old and frequently large – some with over 50 or 60 guest rooms. Many such rooms have been updated to modern expectations, while others are sparse and very 'monastic cell' in style. Overall, there seems to be more dormitory accommodation available in France than in Britain.

Unlike Britain, where the tradition of 'going on retreat' fell from fashion following the Reformation and has only really regained its popularity in this century, France, with its continuous Roman Catholicism, has never lost the tradition. You can expect, therefore, that many French monasteries will expect you to try to participate in the daily round of services and to make your stay more of a spiritual one than just one for relaxation and rest.

While there will be many pleasant culinary surprises, do not expect the meals in monastic France necessarily to reflect the fame of that nation's reputation for cooking. With a few exceptions, vegetarians are in for a difficult time as provision for them is minimal. This has nothing to do with lack of hospitality but everything to do with cultural differences. It is easier now than a few years ago for vegetarians to be catered for in French restaurants so, gradually, the monastic community will probably respond to this growing demand for choice. As to costs for your stay, these are usually in the range 120 to 170 FF per person per day.

The listing is divided alphabetically by the department in France with the department number after it. For example: Calvados (14). Then, on the left-hand side, comes the name of the town or city, followed by the name and address of the retreat centre. The name of the town or city is provided in order to help locate the centre on a map – it does not always correspond exactly with the postal address of the centre. Where the gender of the retreatants is not specified, this indicates that both sexes are welcome.

When applying, please do not telephone but write in the first instance. However, in some cases a fax number is given because it is preferred that you communicate that way if possible. Telephone calls may interrupt religious and other daily routines, but a fax can be dealt with at anytime. Do not assume members of the community will speak English. However, if you must write in English, someone will probably answer your letter.

AIN (01)

Le Plantay
Abbaye Notre-Dame-des-Dombes
Le Plantay
01330 Villars-les-Dombes   Telephone: 74 98 14 40
                                        Fax 74 98 16 70
Roman Catholic. Trappist monks. Receives men, women, groups.
Camping, woods, dormitory & barn. One room for disabled person.
1 hr video on monastery available.

ALLIER (03)

Chantelle
Abbaye Saint-Vincent
Rue Anne de Beauzier
03140 Chantelle   Telephone: 70 56 62 55
Roman Catholic. Receives men, women, accompanied disabled.
Personal talks, meditation.

Dompierre-sur-Besbre
Abbaye Notre Dame de Sept-Fons
03290 Dompierre-sur-Besbre   Telephone: 70 48 14 90
Roman Catholic. Men, religious, for religious retreats only.
Personal talks.

Moulins
Monastère de la Visitation
65, rue des Tanneries
03000 Moulins   Telephone: 70 44 27 43
Roman Catholic. Visitation nuns. 2 rooms for women with enclosure
for a silent retreat.

ALPES-MARITIMES (06)

Carros
Communauté des Carmélites
06510 Carros-Village   Telephone: 93 29 10 71
Roman Catholic. Carmelite nuns. Receives men, women, young
people. 7 rooms for retreats of 15 days. Personal talks, prayers in
chapel with community.

ARDÈCHE (07)

Saint-Étienne-de-Lugdarès
Abbaye Notre-Dame-des-Neiges
07590 Saint Laurent les Bains   Telephone: 66 46 00 68
Roman Catholic. Open Easter to All Saints Day. Receives all, young
people in annex. Group conferences. Setting up high in mountains.
Much silence. Send for brochure.

AUDE (11)

Azille
Monastère Sainte-Claire
Azille
11700 Capendu   Telephone: 68 91 40 24
Roman Catholic. Open to all, for retreat or period of reflection.
Limited number of rooms. Stays of up to 8 days.

Prouilhe
Monastère Sainte-Marie
Prouilhe
11270 Fanjeaux   Telephone: 68 91 40 24
Roman Catholic. A fire destroyed much of this monastery but they
hope to re-open to guests during 1994.

AVEYRON (12)

Espalion
Abbaye Notre-Dame-de-Bonneval
Le Cayrol
12500 Espalion   Telephone: 65 44 01 22
Roman Catholic. Cistercian nuns. Open to all for spiritual retreats.
32 single rooms.

Mur-de-Barrez
Monastère Sainte-Claire
2, rue de la Berque
12600 Mur-de-Barrez   Telephone: 65 66 00 46
Roman Catholic. Receives women and families with children. Pets
welcome. Divine Office in French. Much peace and solitude.

Saint-Sernin-sur-Rance
Monastère Notre-Dame-d'Orient
12380 Saint-Sernin-sur-Rance   Telephone: 65 99 60 88
Roman Catholic. Receives young and not so young, laymen and
laywomen, priests, monks, nuns.

BOUCHES-DU-RHÔNE (13)

Aix-en-Provence
Monastère du Saint-Sacrement
Notre-Dame-de-la-Seds
2, avenue Jean-Dalmas
13090 Aix-en-Provence   Telephone: 42 64 44 36
Roman Catholic.Women and young women, two or three at a time,
are received here by the Carmelite nuns.

Jouques
Abbaye Notre-Dame-de-Fidélité
13490 Jouques   Telephone: 42 57 80 17
Roman Catholic. Receives individuals and groups for Benedictine
hospitality who are searching for peace and calm.

Simiane-Collongue
Communautés Benedictines de Sainte Lioba
Quartier Saint-Germain
13109 Simiane-Collongue   Telephone: 42 22 60 60
Roman Catholic. Open all year to everyone. Receives either those for
a silent retreat in the convent or all others in guest housing. Hill-
walking nearby.

Tarascon
Abbaye Saint-Michel-de-Frigolet
13150 Tarascon-sur-Rhône   Telephone: 90 95 70 07
                                       Fax: 90 95 75
Roman Catholic – a place of herbs set in the beauty of Provence.
Open to all. 38-room accommodation plus a large restaurant which
is also open to visitors and tourists. Well worth just a day visit.

CALVADOS (14)

Bayeux
Monastère de la Sainte-Trinite
48, rue Saint-Loup
B.P. 93
14402 Bayeux Cedex   Telephone: 31 92 02 99
Roman Catholic. Receives women and families. Quiet location and much silence.

Caen
Communaute de Carmélites
51, avenue Clemenceau
14000 Caen   Telephone: 31 93 66 63
Roman Catholic. 5 rooms for women for 5-8 day retreats. Longer stays for those considering a vocation.

Juaye-Mondaye
Abbaye St. Martin de Mondaye
Juaye-Mondaye
14250 Tilly-sur-Seulles   Telephone: 31 92 58 11
                                   Fax: 31 92 08 05
Roman Catholic. Open all year. Receives mostly men. Disabled possible. Special Open Door retreats on Wednesdays in summer. Participation on Divine Office warmly welcomed. A popular place - you need to book about three months in advance.

CHARENTE (16)

Montmoreau-Saint-Cybard
Abbaye Sainte-Marie-de-Maumont
Juignac
16190 Montmoreau-Saint-Cybard   Telephone: 45 60 34 38
Roman Catholic. Open to individuals or groups for stays of up to 10 days. Personal talks by arrangement.

'There must be only one true reality and that it is all taking place within the reality of The One Great Mystery *called* Light of Living Truth.*' Beautiful Painted Arrow*

CHARENTE-MARITIME (17)

La Rochelle
Monastère Sainte-Claire
6, rue de Gué
17000 La Rochelle   Telephone: 46 34 35 21
*Roman Catholic. Open to all women with religious sisters within the
enclosure. Other guests are in self-catering accommodation. There
are 3 hermitages in a large garden and you may stay from 8 days to
1 month. The monastery is closed to guests in winter.*

CHER (18)

Bourges
Carmel
6, rue du Puits-Noir
18000 Bourges   Telephone: 48 24 34 04
Roman Catholic. Open for individual retreats. 4 rooms available.

CORRÈZE (19)

Aubazine
Monastère de la Théophanie
Le Ladeix
19190 Aubazine   Telephone: 55 25 75 67
*Byzantine Catholic nuns. Religious services in French. Receives
men, women, young people, very small groups. 7 single rooms. One
of the nuns speaks English. Warm oriental hospitality from this
community. An old farmhouse, high up in the Massif Central.
Courses on Byzantine spirituality and on the art and theology of
Icons. Vegetarian food on request. A busy place - Easter and summer
time you need to book at least a month in advance.*

CORSE (20)

Erbalunga
Monastère des Bénédictines du Saint-Sacrement
20222 Erbalunga   Telephone: 95 33 22 32
*Roman Catholic. Open from 1 June to 20 September for stays of 2
to 3 weeks. References required before first stay.*

COTE-D'ÔR (21)

Flavignerot
Carmel
Flavignerot
21160 Marsannay-la-Côte   Telephone: 80 42 92 38
Roman Catholic. Receives men and women.

Flavigny-sur-Ozerain
Monastère Saint-Joseph-de-Clairval
21150 Flavigny-sur-Ozerain   Telephone: 80 96 22 31
                                       Fax 80 96 25 29
*Roman Catholic. Open only to men. 17 singles. Stays of less than 5
days.*

CÔTES-DU-NORD (22)

Saint-Brieuc
Carmel
55, rue Pinot-Duclos
22000 Saint-Brieuc   Telephone: 96 94 22 95
Roman Catholic. Receives women for individual retreats.

DORDOGNE (24)

Bergerac
Carmel du Sacré-Coeur
79, rue Valette
24100 Bergerac   Telephone: 53 57 15 33
*Roman Catholic. Open only to women retreatants. Open May and
June. 5 singles.*

Échourgnac
Abbaye Notre-Dame-de-Bonne-Espérance
Échourgnac
24410 Saint-Aulaye   Telephone: 53 80 36 43
Roman Catholic. Trappist nuns. Open to all for spiritual retreats.

DOUBS (25)

Nans-sous-Sainte-Anne
Prieuré Saint-Benoît
Nans-sous-Sainte-Anne
25330 Amancey   Telephone: 81 86 61 79
Roman Catholic. 7 rooms for private retreats.

DRÔME (26)

Aiguebelle
Abbaye Notre-Dame-d'Aiguebelle
Montjoyer
26230 Grignan   Telephone: 75 98 52 33
Roman Catholic. Receives men for retreats.

Crest
Monastère de Sainte-Claire
53, rue des Auberts
26400 Crest   Telephone: 75 25 49 13
Roman Catholic. Receives all. Disabled possible. 100 beds in dormitories. 1 week stays.

Grignan
Prieuré de l'Emmanuel
26230 Grignan   Telephone: 75 46 50 37
Roman Catholic. Open to all. Courses on bibical subjects. Brochure available. 32 beds, camping. Woods and lavender fields all around. Receives women individually or in groups. Wholefood.

Triors
Monastère Notre-Dame-de-Triors
B.P1
26750 Chatillon St. Jean   Telephone: 75 71 43 39
Roman Catholic. Receives everyone. 9 singles, 9 doubles, dormitory. Men in refectory. Others DIY. Brochure of activities available.

EURE (27)

Le Bec-Hellouin
Abbaye Notre-Dame-du-Bec
Le Bec-Hellouin
27800 Brionne   Telephone: 32 44 86 09
Roman Catholic. Open to men individually or in groups. Women guests stay in nearby convent. 30 beds. Men in refectory for meals. A famous Olivetan monastery in a setting of green pastures and small hills, not far from Channel ports.

FINISTÈRE (29)

Landivisiau
Monastère de Kerbenéat
29400 Plounéventer   Telephone: 98 20 47 43
Roman Catholic. Receives women, young people. Separate accommodation for young people. A tree-lined lane leads to the church reflecting a setting for this monastery which is near woods with fields on most sides. A quiet place.

Le Relecq-Kerhuon
Carmel de Brest
88 bis, boulevard Clemenceau
29219 Le Relecq-Kerhuon   Telephone: 98 28 27 93
Roman Catholic. 3 rooms for women only for spiritual retreat. DIY for meals.

GARD (30)

Uzès
Carmel
7, avenue Louis-Alteirac
30700 Uzès   Telephone: 66 22 10 62
Roman Catholic. Open to women only for individual retreats.

GARONNE (HAUTE-) (31)

Blagnac
**Monastère Notre-Dame-des-Sept-Douleurs
et de Sainte-Catherine-de-Sienne
60, avenue Général-Compans
31700 Blagnac**   Telephone: 61 71 47 80
*Roman Catholic. Dominican nuns. Open to all. Guest accommodation
is separate from the monastery. Individual or group retreats with
own leaders for reflection and prayer. Beautiful setting in a quiet
place by the Garronne river.*

Lévignac
**Abbaye Sainte-Marie-du-Désert
Bellegarde-Sainte-Marie
31530 Lévignac**   Telephone: 61 85 61 32
*Roman Catholic. Cistercian monks. 25 rooms for retreatants for up
to 8 days. There is an annual pilgrimage in September for the Nativity
of the Virgin Mary.*

Muret
**Carmel
La Combe-Sainte-Marie
67, chemin Lacombe
31600 Muret**   Telephone: 61 51 03 67
*Roman Catholic. Carmelite nuns who receive women for individual
retreats in solitude.*

GERS (32)

Auch
**Carmel
12, rue Pelletier-d'Oisy
32000 Auch**   Telephone: 62 63 04 76
Roman Catholic. Receives women only for individual retreats.

Saramon
**Monastère Cistercien de Sainte-Marie-de-Boulaur
32450 Boulaur**   Telephone: 62 65 40 07
                                   Fax: 62 65 49 37
*Roman Catholic. Receives women, young people, groups and fami-
lies only - not men. Open May - September. Groups only in winter. 53 beds.*

GIRONDE (33)

Auros
Abbaye de Sainte-Marie-du-Rivet

33124 Auros   Telephone: 56 65 40 10
Roman Catholic. Cistercian nuns. One of the oldest monasteries in France with a 13th century church surrounded by 9th century fortifications. Guest accommodation for individuals, families, and priests in search of calm and repose.

Bordeaux
Monastère de la Visitation
47, cours Marc-Nouaux
33000 Bordeaux   Telephone: 56 44 25 72
Roman Catholic. Receives women only.

HÉRAULT (34)

Le Bousquet-d'Orb
Monastère Orthodoxe Saint-Nicolas
La Dalmerie
34260 Le Bousquet-d'Orb   Telephone: 67 23 41 10
Orthodox - Eastern Rite. Receives men and women. Open Easter to October for spiritual retreats only of up to 7 day stay. 8 beds, camping. Guest dining room. Orthodox only for sacraments.

Roqueredonde
La Borie Noble
38650 Roqueredonde   Telephone: 67 44 09 89
Ecumenical – a Gandhian Ark Community, living a non-violent way of life. Open all year round – receives men, women, young people, families and groups.

Saint-Mathieu-de-Tréviers
Communauté Dominicaine
34270 Saint-Mathieu-de-Tréviers Telephone: 67 55 20 62
Roman Catholic. Open to men, women, families, groups. 18 singles, 24 doubles, some of which are en suite. Stay of up to 3 weeks. Group and personal talks.

ILLE-ET-VILAINE (35)

Plerguer
Notre-Dame-de-Beaufort
35540 Plerguer Telephone: 99 48 07 57
*Roman Catholic. Dominican nuns. Open to all. 20 rooms plus annexe
and dormitory. Silent religious retreats only - not for non-retreatants.
Participation in the Divine Office. The monastery is near a lake.*

INDRE (36)

Fontgombault
Abbaye Notre-Dame-de-Fontgombault
Fontgombault
36220 Tournon-Saint-Martin Telephone: 54 37 12 03
*Roman Catholic. Benedictine monks. Receives men only, in an 11th
century abbey where retreats are in silence and austerity. Retreatants
are expected to be present at the principal Divine Offices.*

Pellevoisin
Monastère des Dominicaines
3 rue Notre Dame
36180 Pellevoisin Telephone: 54 39 00 46
*Roman Catholic. Open to all. Accommodation for 8 for religious
retreats. Open to pilgrims on their journey. Single retreatants may
participate in the choir.*

ISÈRE (38)

Voiron
Monastère de la Visitation
Notre-Dame-du-May
38500 Voiron Telephone: 76 05 26 29
*Roman Catholic. Visitation nuns. Receives individuals and groups
for silent retreats and participation in prayer. Women may make
a retreat within the enclosure for deep silence, meditation, and
prayer. Spiritual guidance in the tradition of St. Francis de Sales is
available if desired.*

JURA (39)

Ougney
Abbaye Notre Dame d'Acey
Vitreux
39350 Gendrey Telephone: 84 81 04 11
Roman Catholic. Cistercian monks. Open to all. 15 rooms. Guests eat separately. Brochure available. A popular place so book several months in advance.

LANDES (40)

Aire-sur- l'Adour
Carmel
6, rue Maubec
B.P. 25
40800 Aire-sur- l'Adour Telephone: 58 71 82 18
Roman Catholic. Receives men and women - but only one person at a time for a religious retreat. Vegetarian food.

LOIRE (42)

Pradines
Abbaye Saint-Joseph-et-Saint-Pierre de Pradines
Pradines
42630 Régny Telephone: 77 64 80 06
Roman Catholic. Receives individuals or groups for retreats in silence.

LOIRE (HAUTE-) (43)

Langeac
Monastère de Sainte-Catherine
2, rue de Pont
43300 Langeac Telephone: 71 77 01 50
Roman Catholic. Dominican nuns. Receives individuals, women religious, priests and very small organised groups for retreats in silence.

Le Puy
Monastère Sainte-Claire
2, rue Sainte-Claire
43000 Le Puy   Telephone: 71 09 17 47
Roman Catholic. Open from June to September and in school
holidays for individuals in search of calm.

LOIRE-ATLANTIQUE (44)

La Meilleraye-de-Bretagne
Abbaye Notre-Dame-de-Melleray
La Meilleraye-de-Bretagne
44520 Moisdon-la-Rivière   Telephone: 40 55 20 01
Roman Catholic. Cistercian trappist monks.Receives men for spiri-
tual retreats and visits for peace and reflection. Silent retreats.

LOIRET (45)

Saint-Jean-de-Braye
Monastère des Bénédictines de Notre-Dame-du-Calvaire
65, avenue de Verdun
45801 Saint-Jean-de-Braye Cedex   Telephone: 38 61 43 05
Roman Catholic. Benedictine nuns. Religious retreats only. Receives
women and young women. Weekends for young women within
cloister for those considering a vocation. Not a particularly quiet
situation as it is in a busy town.

MAINE-ET-LOIRE (49)

Angers
Prieuré de Notre-Dame-du-Calvaire
8, rue Vauvert
49100 Angers   Telephone: 41 87 76 28
Roman Catholic. Benedictine nuns. Individuals or in small groups
with retreats within the enclosure for women religious and young
women who want to participate more fully in the community's life of
prayer.

Bégrolles-en-Mauges
Abbaye de Bellefontaine
49122 Bégrolles-en-Mauges   Telephone: 41 63 81 60
Roman Catholic. Receives men and women. 20 singles, 25 doubles,
dormitory for 50. May be able to help with work of community.
Vegetarians can be catered for. Brochure available.

                                          MANCHE (50)
Avranches
Monastere du Carmel
59, boulevard du Luxembourg
50300 Avranches   Telephone: 33 58 23 66
Roman Catholic. Receives women young women, small groups
for retreats. 4 room in monastery, annexe for groups of up to 12.
Retreatants are expected to live according to the daily routine of
pray in the monastic life of the community. Set between a busy road
and quiet countryside.

Le Mont-Saint-Michel
Communauté de l'Abbaye
B.P. 3
50116 Le Mont-Saint-Michel   Telephone: 33 60 14 47
Roman Catholic. Benedictine monks. Receives men and women. 12
beds for spiritual retreats only. Guests must attend all Divine
Offices. Groups are only received who are part of a church or
religious organisation. A famous setting and place which is still one
of the great national tourist attractions of France.

Saint-James
Prieuré Saint-Jacques
50240 Saint-James   Telephone: 33 48 31 39
Roman Catholic. This community of nuns receives individuals and
religious who want to participate in the community's life of prayer.

Saint-Pair-sur-Mer
Carmel
213, route de Lézeaux
50380 Saint-Pair-sur-Mer   Telephone: 33 50 12 00
Roman Catholic. Receives individual retreatants.

MARNE (51)

Fismes
Abbaye Notre-Dame-d'Igny
Arcis-le-Ponsart
51170 Fismes Telephone: 26 78 08 40
Roman Catholic. Open for spiritual retreats only, for stays of up to one week. Participation in the Divine Office with help from one of the sisters in this Cistercian community. Brochure available.

Reims
Monastère Sainte-Claire (Soeurs Pauvres)
13, avenue Roger-Salengro
51430 Tinqueux Telephone: 26 08 23 15
Roman Catholic. St. Clare nuns. Open to all. 55 beds including annexe, barn, and dormitory. Closes last two weeks of July.

Saint-Thierry
Monastère des Bénédictines
51220 Saint-Thierry Telephone: 26 03 10 72
Roman Catholic. Limited number of rooms for individuals or group retreats. 16 singles, 6 doubles. Two rooms on ground floor for disabled.

MAYENNE (53)

Craon
Monastère des Bénédictines du Saint-Sacrement
15, rue de la Libération
53400 Craon Telephone: 43 06 13 38
Roman Catholic. Receives women, young women, families, and group retreatants. 14 rooms plus 2 dormitories, library. Some rooms face the road, some the garden. Divine Office in Gregorian chant. Women may make a retreat within the enclosure.

MEURTRE-ET-MOSELLE (54)

Nancy
Monastère de la Visitation
64, rue Marquette
54000 Nancy Telephone: 83 96 63 83
Roman Catholic. Receives women and religious only for individual retreats.

MORBIHAN (56)

Bréhan
Abbaye Notre-Dame-de-Timadeuc
Bréhan
56580 Rohan   Telephone: 97 51 50 29
Roman Catholic. Receives men and women.

Campénéac
Abbaye-la-Joie-Notre-Dame
Campénéac 56800   Telephone: 97 93 42 07
*Roman Catholic. Cistercian nuns. Receives men and women - not
families - groups for conferences. 30 rooms, 2 dormitories, camping,
accepts disabled. Very quiet and close to the Forest of Broceliande.
The nuns have a visual exhibition on the monastic life.*

Plouharnel
Abbaye Sainte-Anne-de-Kergonan
56340 Plouharnel   Telephone: 97 52 30 75
*Roman Catholic. Benedictine monks. Receives men individually.
15 singles. Meals in refectory. Divine Office in Gregorian chant.
Quiet location close to the sea.*

MOSELLE (57)

Delme
Abbaye d'Oriocourt
57590 Delme   Telephone: 87 01 31 67
*Roman Catholic. Benedictine nuns. Receives men, women and groups.
No families. 10 rooms for those seeking peace and solitude.*

NORD (59)

Le Mont-des-Cats
Abbaye Sainte-Marie-du-Mont
Le Mont-des-Cats, Godewaersvelde
59270 Bailleul   Telephone: 28 42 52 50
*Roman Catholic. Open to all. 30 rooms. Meals taken in silence.
Countryside location.*

Moustier-en-Fagne
Prieuré Saint-Dodon
Moustier-en-Fagne
59132 Trelon   Telephone: 27 61 81 28
*Roman Catholic. This is a Vita et Pax community of nuns so you will
be assured of a warm welcome in a very homely atmosphere. Closed
September and October. Receives men, women, young people, groups,
no families. 11 rooms in excellent taste plus separate DIY annexe for
groups with own leader. Accompanied disabled accepted. Stays up
to 15 days. There is a Byzantine chapel and icon painting is a
speciality of the community. A very quiet setting near a small river
with lots of trees and much peace. It is possible to walk into Belgium
from here.*

Mouvaux
Monastère de la Visitation
192, rue Lorthiois
59420 Mouvaux   Telephone: 20 26 94 34
Roman Catholic. Receives individuals or small groups.

OISE (60)

Beauvais
Monastère du Carmel-Saint-Joseph
62, rue Louis-Prache
60000 Beauvais   Telephone: 44 45 29 70
*Roman Catholic. Individual retreats outside the enclosure. Small
group retreats by special arrangement.*

ORNE (61)

Alençon
Monastère Sainte-Claire
7, rue de la Demi-Lune
61000 Alençon   Telephone: 33 26 14 58
*Roman Catholic. St. Clare nuns. Receives women and young women.
6 rooms. A fairly noisy location in town.*

Soligny-la-Trappe
Abbaye Notre Dame de la Trappe
Soligny-la-Trappe
61380 Moulins-la-Marche   Telephone: 33 34 50 44
                                     Fax: 33 34 98 57
*Roman Catholic. Trappist monks. Receives men only – individually
or in groups. 50 rooms. Guest accommodation separate from
monastery. Accepts disabled. Retreats in silence. A very quiet
location in a forest.*

                                     PAS-DE-CALAIS (62)
Béthune
Monastère du Carmel
23, rue Fernand-Fanien
Fouquières-lès-Lens
62232 Annezin   Telephone: 21 68 11 22
Roman Catholic. 4 rooms for retreats in silence, prayer and solitude.

Boulogne-sur-Mer
Monastère de la Visitation
9, rue Maquétra
62220 Saint-Martin-Boulogne   Telephone: 21 31 35 88
*Roman Catholic. Receives religious, women. Retreats in silence.
Participation in Divine Office.*

Wisques
Abbaye Saint-Paul
Wisques
62219 Longuenesse   Telephone: 21 95 11 04
*Roman Catholic. Benedictine monks. Receives men only – individually
or in groups. 23 rooms and camping available for young people.
Brochure available.*

Chamalières
Monastère des Clarisses-Capucines
11, avenue de Villars
63407 Chamalières Cedex   Telephone: 73 37 73 11
Roman Catholic. One of only three Capucine monasteries in France.
The nuns are enclosed. Franciscan spirituality. Receives everyone
for individual retreats. 8 rooms. Brochure available.

Randol
Abbaye Notre-Dame-de Randol
63450 Saint-Amant-Tallende   Telephone: 73 39 31 00
Roman Catholic. Benedictine monks. Receives men. A new monastery
opened in 1971 of very modern architectual design, dramatically set
on the very edge of a steep gorge. A similiar looking place to
Prinknash Abbey in England- but much grander and more imposing.

Anglet
Convent des Bernardines Notre Dame de Refuge
Avenue de Montbrun
64600 Anglet   Telephone: 59 63 84 34
Roman Catholic. Bernardine nuns. Receives women only for silent
retreat. 5 single cells, meals with community. The food is from their
own fields and gardens.

Orthez
Monastère Sainte-Claire
35, rue Saint-Gilles
64300 Orthez   Telephone: 59 69 46 55
Roman Catholic. The nuns have a few rooms for self-catering stays.
Participation in prayers of the community.

Urt
Abbaye Notre-Dame-de-Belloc
64240 Urt   Telephone: 59 29 65 55
Roman Catholic. Benedictine monks. Receives men only. 36 rooms.
Disabled accepted. Conferences possible. Personal talks, group
discussions, directed courses. Programme of activities – send for
brochure. Also Benedictine sisters are at same address so please
write to them for details of their hospitality.

Lourdes
Carmel Notre-Dame-de-Lourdes
17, route de Pau
65100 Lourdes   Telephone: 62 94 26 67
Roman Catholic. Receives men and women for day retreats and in
the summer months for longer stays. Lourdes is one of the greatest
places of pilgrimage in Europe so there are always crowds. In spite
of this, the Shrine at Lourdes and its huge church are well worth a
visit. Forget the streets lined with tourist merchandise and religious
trinkets and concentrate on the prayerful atmosphere of the Shrine
with its many candles of inspiring light.

Tournay
Abbaye Notre-Dame
65190 Tournay   Telephone: 62 35 70 21
Roman Catholic. Benedictine monks. Receives men and women - no
families. 36 singles plus dormitories. Men in refectory, women
guests eat separately. Quiet location, close to a river.

Rosheim
Monastère Notre Dame du Sacre Coeur
Hotellerie Notre Dame de la Source
3 rue Saint-Benoît
67560 Rosheim   Telephone: 88 50 41 67
Roman Catholic. Benedictine nuns who receive men and women all
year round. 15 rooms plus dormitories. Very modern in newly
converted farm buildings. Divine Office in Gregorian chant. Courses
in Gregorian chant are available during the year. Walks in forest
and countryside. Brochure available.

Landser
Monastère Saint-Alphonse
Landser
68440 Habsheim   Telephone: 89 81 30 10
Roman Catholic. The nuns receive women. 6 rooms. Quiet location
in country village. You may help in the garden.

Oelenberg
Abbaye de Notre-Dame-d'Oelenberg
68950 Reiningue   Telephone: 89 81 91 23
Roman Catholic. Receives men and women – individually or in groups.

Sigolsheim
Monastère de Marie-Médiatrice
5, rue Oberhof
68240 Sigolsheim   Telephone: 89 78 23 24
Roman Catholic. Receives women only.

SAÔNE-ET-LOIRE (71)

Autun
Carmel 1, rue Chaffaut
71400 Autun   Telephone: 85 52 01 29
Roman Catholic. Receives men and women.

Mazille
Carmel de la Paix
Mazille
B.P. 10
71250 Cluny   Telephone: 85 50 80 54
                                       Fax: 85 50 81 43
Roman Catholic. Carmelite nuns. Open to all. 50 rooms for retreats in silence. Participation in Divine Office and help with work of community. Wholefood.

Paray-le-Monial
Monastère de la Visitation
13, rue de la Visitation
71600 Paray-le-Monial   Telephone: 85 81 09 95
Roman Catholic. Visitation nuns. Open to all but there is no guest accommodation so you have to stay in local village and attend religious services in the convent. The Chapel is open all year.

Taizé
Communauté de Taizé
71250 Taizé   Telephone: 85 50 30 00
*Ecumenical. In founding the Taizé Community, Brother Roger
attempted to open ways to heal the divisions between Christians, and
through reconciliation of Christians, to overcome certain conflicts
in humanity. Today the Community includes both Protestant and
Catholic brothers from over twenty countries. This is one of the most
popular retreat places in the Western world - in some years as many
as 6000 visit in a single week. Taizé receives men, women and
especially young people. 30 rooms plus dormitories, camping, and
caravans. While all activities take place in Taizé itself, most adult
accommodation is in villages nearby. Accepts disabled and families
with children. Personal talks, meditation, and group discussions.
There are special meetings for different age groups - for example,
special activities for younger people and over-60 meetings. Everyone
eats together and the food is simple. No provisions for vegetarians.
Send for information which lists the various meetings and gives
important details which you need to know before deciding to go
there. You must write at least two months before your intended stay
and wait for a reply before making any firm arrangements. It is so
crowded in summer that older people are advised to come before or
after that period. Yet, there is also the possibility of finding peace
and solitude at Taizé.* **Highly recommended.**

Venière
Abbaye Notre-Dame
Venière
71700 Tournus   Telephone: 85 51 05 85
*Roman Catholic. Receives men and women – individually and in
groups.*

SARTHE

Rouillon
Carmel
Vaujoubert-Notre-Dame
72700 Rouillon   Telephone: 43 24 17 68
Roman Catholic. Receives men, women and groups of young people.

Solesmes
Abbaye Saint-Pierre-de-Solesmes
72300 Sablé-sur-Sarthe   Telephone: 43 95 03 08
Roman Catholic. Receives men only.

Saint-Pierre-d'Albigny
Monastère de la Visitation
Clos Minjoud
73250 Saint-Pierre-d'Albigny   Telephone: 79 28 50 12
*Roman Catholic. The sisters receive up to three women only within
the enclosure where there is a large park. Individual retreats outside
the enclosure are for both men and women - one person or a couple
at a time. There is a small garden. Mountain walking near at hand.*

Tamié
Abbaye Notre-Dame de Tamié
Plancherine
73200 Albertville   Telephone: 79 32 42 01
*Roman Catholic. The monks receive men, women, and groups. 27
rooms. Families are also welcome but stay in a separate chalet. You
may participate in the Divine Office and the work of the community.
Guests eat separately. Vegetarian provision possible. Personal talks
and directed courses. Quiet location in mountains.*

Annecy
Monastère de la Visitation
11, avenue de la Visitation
74000 Annecy   Telephone: 50 45 20 30
Roman Catholic. Receives women only.

Thonon-les-Bains
Monastère de la Visitation
Marclaz
74200 Thonon-les-Bains   Telephone: 50 70 34 46
*Roman Catholic. Receives men, women and families (but without
young babies).*

Paris
Abbaye Sainte-Marie
3, rue de la Source
75016 Paris   Telephone: 45 25 30 07
Roman Catholic. Benedictine monks. Receives men only for spiritual
retreats - not for tourist stays. This is the only Benedictine monastery
in Paris. Personal talks and meditation. Good library. Everyone eats
together. This is a refuge of peace and calm in the midst of a rushing
and noisy city.

Monastère de Bethléem
Notre-Dame-de-la-Présence-de-Dieu
2, rue Mesnil
75116 Paris   Telephone: 45 01 24 48
Roman Catholic. The sisters receive men and women who want to
participate in silent prayer or in the liturgy of the community. There
is no guest accommodation at the monastery. The community lives as
much as possible in the spirit of the desert in the middle of this great
city. From Sunday night to Monday noon they try to live out this
special spiritual practice and the church is closed during this period.

Monastère de l'Adoration-Réparatrice
39, rue Gay-Lussac
75005 Paris   Telephone: 43 26 75 75
Roman Catholic. Receives men and women for individual retreats.

Monastère de la Visitation
68, avenue Denfert-Rochereau
74014 Paris   Telephone: 43 27 12 90
Roman Catholic. Receives women only.

Saint-Wandrille-Rançon
Abbaye Saint-Wandrille
76490 Saint-Wandrille   Telephone: 35 96 23 11
Roman Catholic. The monks receive men, women, young people and
groups. Up to 8 day stays. 35 rooms. Men eat with the community.
Women and couples eat separately. Personal talks, group discussion.
A quiet location in a village.

SEINE-ET-MARNE (77)

Brou-sur-Chantereine
Prieuré St Joseph
1, avenue Victor-Thiebaut
77177 Brou-sur-Chantereine   Telephone: 60 20 11 20
Roman Catholic. Receives all in guest house for individual or group retreats.

Faremoutiers
Abbaye Notre-Dame-et-Saint-Pierre
1 ruye Fenelon Desfourneaux
77515 Faremoutiers   Telephone: 64 04 20 37
Roman Catholic. Benedictine contemplative nuns. Receive women and groups of up to15 in self-catering accommodation. Garden and library. Some liturgy is in Gregorian chant. Brochure available. Approximately 55 km from Paris.

Jouarre
Abbaye Notre-Dame-de-Jouarre
6, rue Montmorin
77640 Jouarre   Telephone: 60 22 06 11
Roman Catholic. The sisters receive women, families, and groups. 40 singles, 9 doubles. Guests eat separately. There is a Merovingian crypt of special interest. Brochure available. Quiet village setting.

YVELINES (78)

Bonnelles
Monastère des Orantes-de-l'Assomption
Chemin de Noncienne
78830 Bonnelles   Telephone: 30 41 32 76
Roman Catholic. Receives men and women – individually or in groups.

SEVRES (DEUX-) (79)

Niort
Monastere du Carmel
157, rue de Strasbourg
79000 Niort   Telephone: 49 24 18 72
Roman Catholic. Carmelite nuns who receive women only. 3 beds. Retreats in silence and prayer. Participation in Divine Office. A town location.

TARN (81)

Dourgne
Abbaye Saint-Benoît-d'en-Calcat
81110 Dourgne   Telephone: 63 50 32 37
Roman Catholic. Open to all. 40 singles, 5 doubles. Accepts disabled. Personal talks and directed courses. Guests eat separately. A quiet location in the contryside.

TARN-ET-GARONNE (82)

Verdun-sur-Garonne
Abbaye Saint-Pierre
82600 Mas-Grenier
Verdun-sur-Garonne   Telephone: 63 02 51 22
Roman Catholic. Benedictine nuns who receive women, families and groups, for up to 15 days. 33 singles, 2 doubles. For organised retreat groups, accommodation is next door in the Acceuil St. Pierre.

VAR (83)

Cotignac
Prieuré-la-Font-Saint-Joseph-du-Bessillon
83570 Cotignac   Telephone: 94 04 63 44
Roman Catholic. Receives women only.

Saint-Maximin-La-Sainte-Baume
Monastère Sainte-Marie-Madeleine
Route de Barjols
83470 Saint-Maximin-La-Sainte-Baume Telephone: 94 78 04 71
Roman Catholic. Open to all, but closed in September and October. Stays of up to 15 days. 5 singles, 5 doubles plus dormitory. Everyone eats together.

VAUCLUSE (84)

Montfavet
Monastere Sainte-Claire-de-Notre-Dame-des-Miracles
La Verdière
B.P. 28
84140 Montfavet   Telephone: 90 31 01 55
Roman Catholic. Receives men and women.

VENDÉE (85)

Chavagnes-en-Paillers
Carmel de la Fouchardière
Chavagnes-en-Paillers
85250 Saint-Fulgent   Telephone: 51 42 21 80
Roman Catholic. Receives men and women.

La Roche-sur-Yon
Monastère Sainte-Claire-de-Saint-Joseph
36, rue Abbé-Pierre-Arnaud
85000 La Roche-sur-Yon   Telephone: 51 37 10 13
Roman Catholic. Receives couples and women.

Les Sables-d'Olonne
Monastère de la Passion
1, rue du Petit-Montauban
La Chaume
85100 Les Sables-d'Olonne   Telephone: 51 95 19 26
Roman Catholic. Receives men and women.

VIENNE (86)

Ligugé
Abbaye Saint-Martin
86240 Ligugé   Telephone: 49 55 21 12
*Roman Catholic. Benedictine monks. Open to all. 20 single rooms,
15 doubles, dormitories and camping. Gregorian chant in Divine
Office.*

Poitiers
Abbaye Sainte-Croix   Telephone: 49 37 51 18
86280 Saint-Benoît   49 88 57 33
*Roman Catholic. Benedictine nuns who receive women, young
people, families, and groups for spiritual retreat and prayer only. 20
single rooms, 4 doubles. Personal discussions and group talks as
arranged in advance. There is a special programme for young
women 20-35 years for participating more fully in the life of the
community which has been going since the 14th century. Brochure
available. Quiet location in countryside.*

Saint-Julien l'Ars
Monastere de l'Annonciation
11 rue du Parc
86800 Saint-Julien l'Ars Telephone: 49 56 71 01
Roman Catholic. Benedictine nuns. Receives women, families and very small groups. Young women may participate in work of community. Personal talks and groups discussions. Quiet. In a country village. Brochure available.

Ubexy
Abbaye Notre-Dame-de-Saint-Joseph
88130 Ubexy Telephone: 29 38 04 32
Roman Catholic. Cistercian nuns. Receives men and women, but not families. 19 single rooms, 8 doubles plus dormitory. Guests eat separately. Personal talks with arrangements for group discussion.

La Pierre-qui-Vire
Abbaye Sainte-Marie de-la-Pierre-qui-Vire
89630 Saint-Léger-Vauban Telephone: 86 32 24 06
Roman Catholic. Open to men and women over 18 years, groups. 74 single rooms, 12 doubles plus dormitories. Participation in Divine Office and guests may help with the work of the community. There is a library, a church and two oratories for private prayer. Guests eat separately with some meals taken in silence. A very peaceful location in the woods.

Sens
Monastere de la Nativité
105, rue Victor-Guichard
89100 Sens Telephone: 86-65-13-41
Roman Catholic. Dominican nuns. Receives women with men accepted in groups or in families. Also welcomes accompanied children. There is accommodation for 80. Retreatants help with washing up and bed making. Vegetarian food by arrangement. Quiet location on the edge of a town. Brochure available.

TERRITOIRE DE BELFORT (90)

Lepuix-Gy
Prieuré Saint-Benoît-de-Chauveroche
Lepuix-Gy
90200 Giromagny   Telephone: 84 29 01 57
Roman Catholic. Receives men, women, and groups for individual retreats.

ESSONNE (91)

Évry
Monastère de la Croix
Cours Monseigneur-Romero
91000 Évry   Telephone: 64 97 22 72
Roman Catholic. Receives men and women.

Limon Vauhallan
Abbaye Saint-Louis-du-Temple
Limon
91430 Vauhallan
Telephone: 69 85 21 00
Roman Catholic. Benedictine nuns. Receives men and women in small groups or as individuals under guidance of one of the sisters. 20 single rooms, dormitory, library. The Abbey was founded in memory of the French royal family who were imprisoned in the temple tower during the revolution. Glass windows designed by Maire Genevieve Gallois (1888 - 1962). Peaceful village location.

Soisy-sur-Seine
Communauté de l'Épiphanie
Avenue du Général-de-Gaulle
91450 Soisy-sur-Seine   Telephone: 60 75 32 59
Roman Catholic. Receives men and women – individually and in groups.

Vanves
Prieuré Sainte-Bathilde
7, rue d'Issy
92170 Vanves   Telephone: 46 42 46 20
Roman Catholic. Benedictine nuns receive women only. Closed July
and August. 10 single rooms. Personal talks and group discussions.
Library and bookshop. Quiet location but in a city. Receives men and
women – individually or in small groups.

Spain

Extrovert and fun-loving Spain boasts a treasure house of peaceful and welcoming monasteries still almost unknown to the tourist. The Spanish government's tourist department is aware of the growing interest in retreats as a form of 'holiday' and have now taken steps to make information available. It is early days yet and many of the Spanish tourist offices may not know what you are talking about when you ask for details - but they do have the information, so persist. The key to getting it is to mention the pilgrims way to Santiago de Compostela which, if you are at all religious, is one of the best routes along which to seek monastic hospitality for a retreat. You could try staying at one of the hotel-type paradores, the **Parador de Santo Domingo de la Calzada**, Plaza del Santo No. 3, Santo Domingo de la Calzada (Tel: 941 340 300) and venturing out from there to two famous but peaceful monasteries. The **Monastery of Santo Domingo de Silos** is south of Burgos while the other, the **Monastery of San Millan de la Cogolla**, is east of Burgos and a place that those interested in art and architecture will greatly enjoy. All of these places are in or near Spain's wine-growing area of La Rioja.

Many of the monasteries of Spain receive guests of only one gender and the accommodation is usually simple and the food very plain. As to charges for your stay, most ask for nothing and you should leave a voluntary donation. If charges are made, these are likely to range between 800 and 1500 pesetas a day. Spain is still a deeply Catholic country and most monastic communities will expect you to observe their silence and to respect their way of daily religious life. Having said that, you will find a warm welcome and peaceful hospitality in some of the most beautiful surroundings in Europe.

Barcelona
Abadia de Montserrat
Montserrat
Barcelona   Telephone: 93 835 02 51
Roman Catholic. A Benedictine community receiving men and women in a small guest house situated in a marvellous mountain setting.

Burgos
Abadia de San Pedro de Cardena
Burgos   Telephone: 947 29 00 03
Roman Catholic. A Cistercian abbey receiving men only, for a stay of up to eight days. 24 rooms within the monastery. Much silence and an atmosphere of meditation.

Abadia de Santo Domingo de Silos
Santo Domingo de Silos
Burgos   Telephone: 947 38 07 68
Roman Catholic.. Benedictine abbey receiving men only. 21 rooms
which are much above the average in comfort with individual
bathrooms and central heating. There is a peaceful and serious
atmosphere here with the Divine Office in Gregorian chant. The
Holy Week religious services are impressive and justly famous.

Monasterio de Las Huelgas
Burgos   Telephone: 947 20 16 30
Roman Catholic. Receives women in an annexe guest house.

Monasterio de Palacios de Benaver
Palacios de Benaver
Burgos   Telephone: 947 45 10 09
Roman Catholic. Receives both men and women. A convent with four
guest rooms with Gregorian chant at the services.

Caceros
Monasterio de Yusto
Cuacos
Caceros   Telephone: 927 48 05 30
Roman Catholic. Receives men for stays of up to a week.

Cantabria
Abadia de Viaceli
Corbreces
Cantabria   Telephone: 942 72 50 17
Roman Catholic. Cistercian community receiving men only for stays
of up to one week. This is a place to stay if you are going on a serious
religious retreat and not just to rest and relax. The atmosphere is
strict, silent, and deeply spiritual.

La Coruna
Monasterio de Sobrado de los Monjes
Sobrado
Near La Coruna   Telephone: 981 78 90 09
Roman Catholic. Receives men only.

Leon
Monasterio de Carrizo
Carrizo
Leon   Telephone: 987 35 70 55
Roman Catholic. Cistercian nuns. Receives men and women. 4
rooms for a maximum stay of eight days. The convent closes early in
the evening and guests are expected to respect the religious timetable.

Monasterio de San Pedro de las Duenas
Sahagun
Leon   Telephone: 987 78 01 50
Roman Catholic. Benedictine nuns who receive both men and women
in a guest house. Visitors may come here just to relax and rest or for
a retreat for which the charges are lower.

Madrid
Monasterio de El Paular
Rascafria
Madrid   Telephone: 91 869 1425
Roman Catholic. Receives men for stays of up to ten days.

Navarre
Abadia de Leyre
Yesa
Navarre   Telephone: 948 88 40 11
Roman Catholic. A Benedictine abbey lodging men only in monastic
cells for a religious retreat. Both men and women can stay in an
annexe guest house where the atmosphere is relaxed and more
independent.

Monasterio de la Oliva
Cascastillo
Navarre   Telephone: 948 72 50 06
Roman Catholic. Receives both men and women in a place which is
a wonderful example of Cistercian architecture. Peaceful but busy
and hard working atmosphere.

Palencia
Monasterio de San Isidro de Duenas
Venta de Banos
Palencia   Telephone: 988 77 07 01
Roman Catholic. A trappist monastery open to men and married
couples seeking a retreat.

Salamanca
Convento de Carmel Dascatros
Las Mostas
La Alberca
Salamanca   Telephone: 923 43 71 33
Roman Catholic. A strictly religious place where men only may go for
spiritual retreat and then only by prior request and permission. It is
not open to tourists. The film director, Luis Bunuel, stayed here once
and fell in love with the beautiful Las Batuecas valley where the
monastery is situated. He called it a paradise on earth.

Segovia
Monasterio de Santa Maria de El Parral
Segovia   Telephone: 911 43 12 98
Roman Catholic. Receives men in three ensuite rooms for stays of up
to a week for those seeking a spiritual retreat. Guests can either
follow the monks' routine and take meals with them or be independent.

Soria
Monasterio de Santa Maria de Huerta
Santa Maria de Huerta
Soria   Telephone: 975 32 70 02
Roman Catholic. Cistercian monks receiving men only in eight
rooms. Best to write first.

Tarragona
Abadia de Santa Maria de Poblet
Espluga de Francoli
Tarragona   Telephone: 977 87 00 89
Roman Catholic. Receives men only within the abbey itself and
guests are expected to keep to the community's monastic timetable.
Everyone eats together in the refectory.

The National Retreat Association
Liddon House
24 South Audley Street
London W1Y 5DL   Telephone: 071-493 3534

The Inter-Faith Network for the United Kingdom
5-7 Tavistock Place
London WC1H 9SS   Telephone: 071-387 0008

World Congress of Faiths
The Inter-Faith Fellowship
28 Powis Gardens
London W11 1JG   Telephone: 071-727 2607

Buddhist Society
58 Ecclestone Square
London SW1 1PH   Telephone: 081-834 5858

London Buddhist Centre
51 Roman Road
London E2 OHU   Telephone: 081-981 1225

Amaravati Buddhist Centre
Great Gaddesden
Hemel Hempstead
Herts. HP1 3BZ   Telephone: 044 284 2455

The Islamic Centre
146 Park Road
London NW8 7RG   Telephone: 071-724 3363

National Council of Hindu Temples
559 St Alban's Road
Watford
Herts. WD2 6JH   Telephone: 0923 674 168

Maps

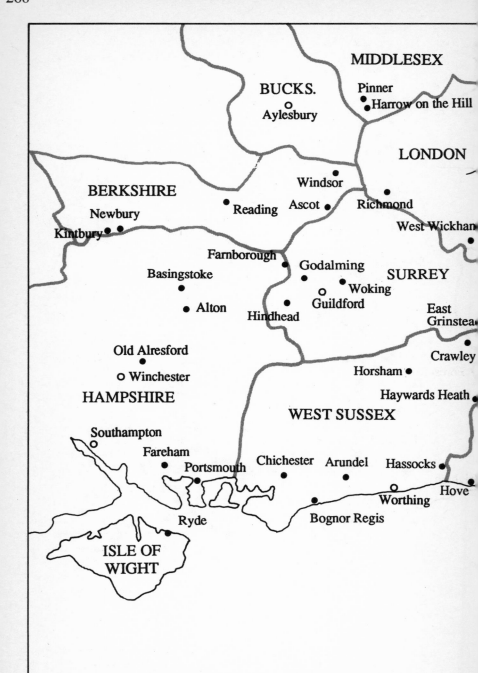

Westgate on Sea

Margate

Ramsgate

Maidstone

Sevenoaks

Canterbury

KENT

Forest Row

Folkestone

Heathfield

EAST SUSSEX

Brighton

Hastings

Eastbourne

Retreat centre = ●
Main town   = O

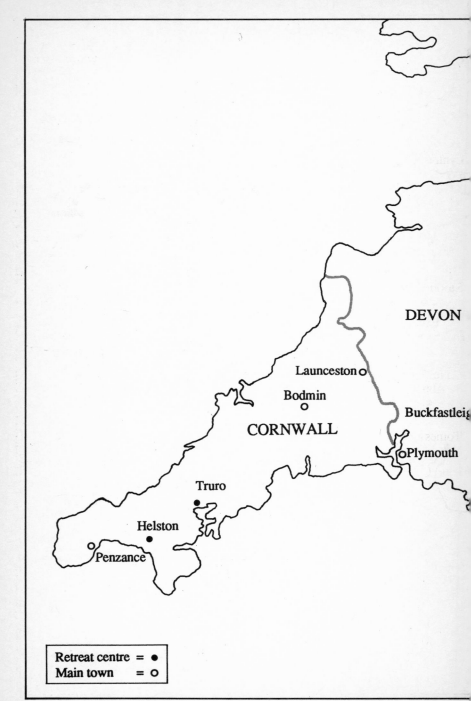

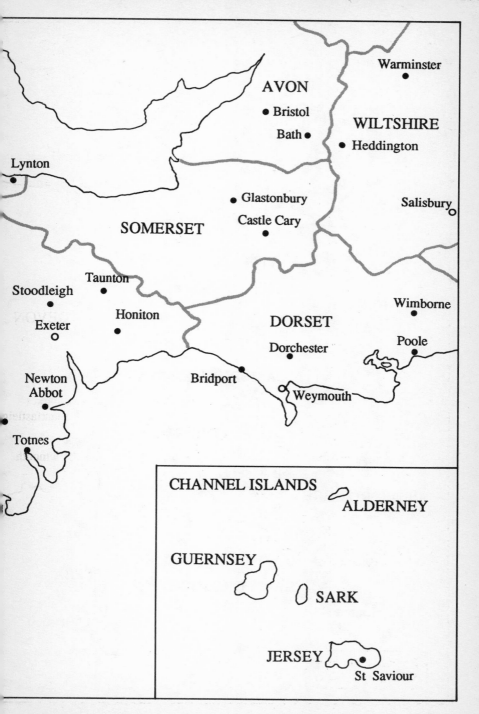

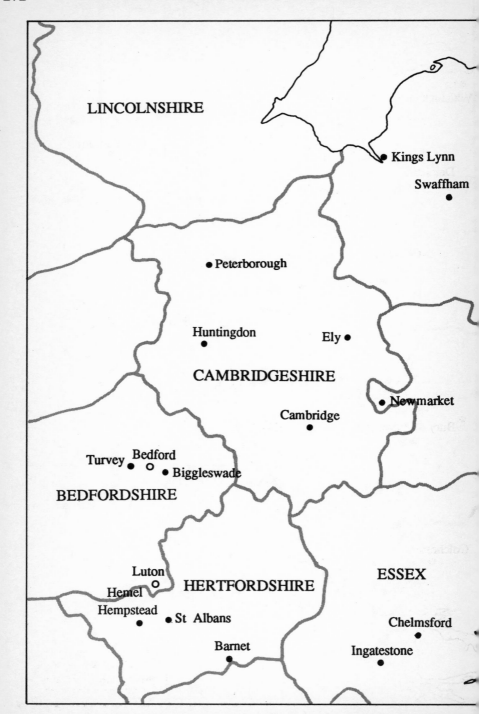

LINCOLNSHIRE

Kings Lynn

Swaffham

Peterborough

Huntingdon

Ely

CAMBRIDGESHIRE

Newmarket

Cambridge

Turvey Bedford

Biggleswade

BEDFORDSHIRE

Luton

Hemel

Hempstead

HERTFORDSHIRE

St Albans

Barnet

ESSEX

Chelmsford

Ingatestone

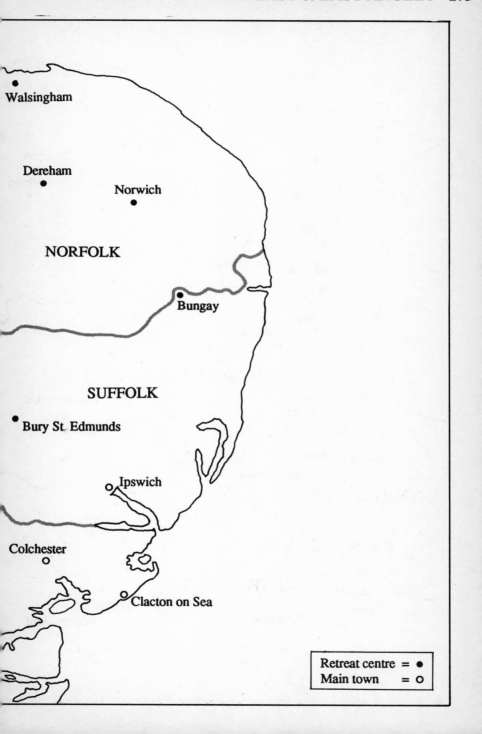

Walsingham

Dereham

Norwich

NORFOLK

Bungay

SUFFOLK

Bury St. Edmunds

Ipswich

Colchester

Clacton on Sea

Retreat centre = ●
Main town   = ○

CENTRAL ENGLAND

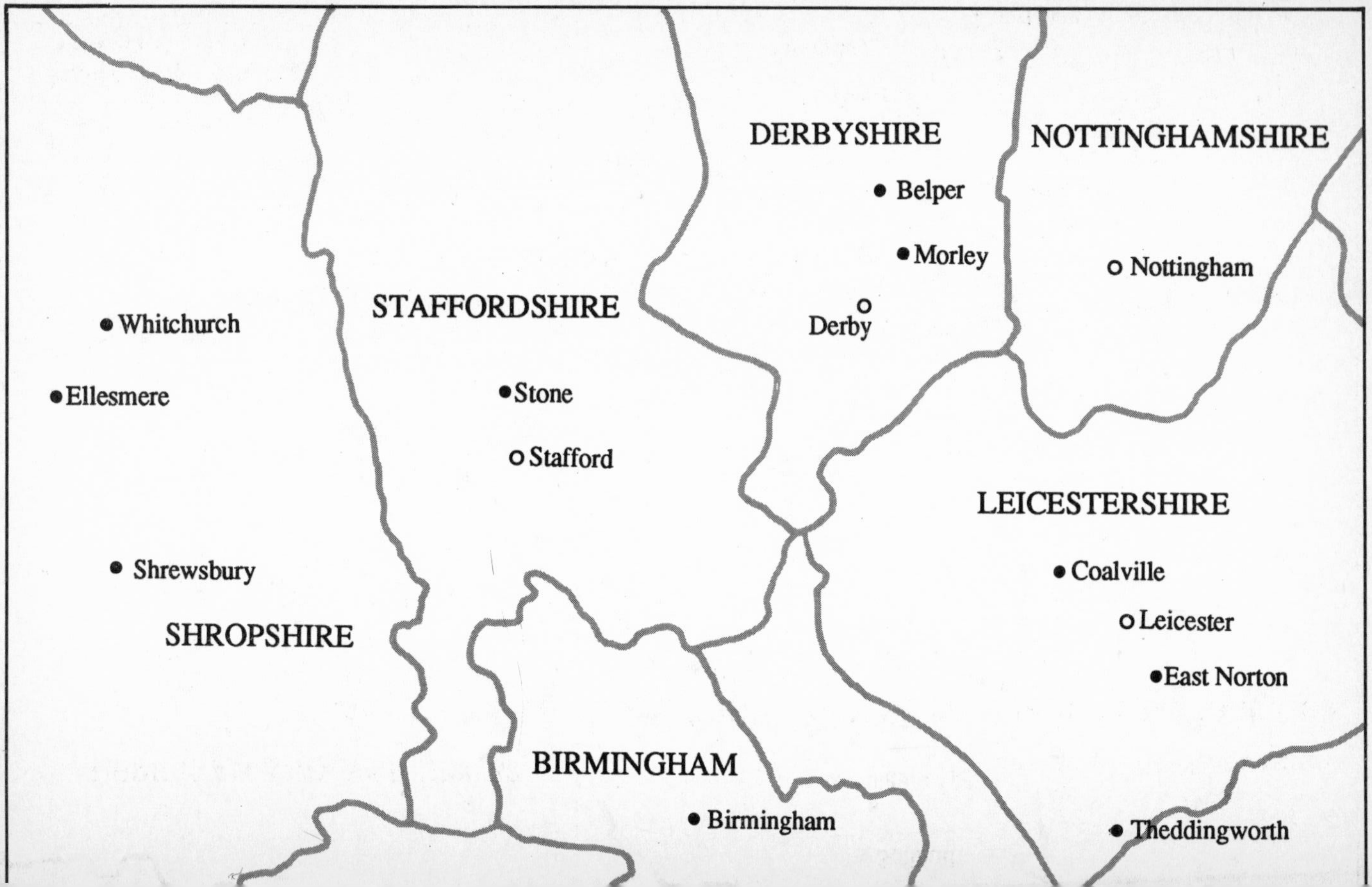

DERBYSHIRE
NOTTINGHAMSHIRE
Belper
Morley
Nottingham
Derby
STAFFORDSHIRE
Whitchurch
Ellesmere
Stone
Stafford
LEICESTERSHIRE
Shrewsbury
Coalville
Leicester
SHROPSHIRE
East Norton
BIRMINGHAM
Birmingham
Theddingworth

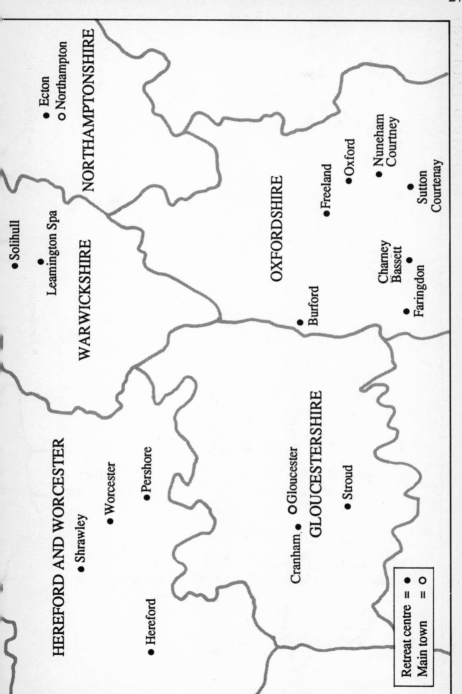

HEREFORD AND WORCESTER

- Shrawley
- Worcester
- Pershore
- Hereford

WARWICKSHIRE

- Solihull
- Leamington Spa

NORTHAMPTONSHIRE

- Ecton
- o Northampton

OXFORDSHIRE

- Freeland
- Oxford
- Nuneham Courtney
- Sutton Courtenay
- Charney Bassett
- Faringdon
- Burford

GLOUCESTERSHIRE

- Cranham
- o Gloucester
- Stroud

Retreat centre = ●
Main town = ○

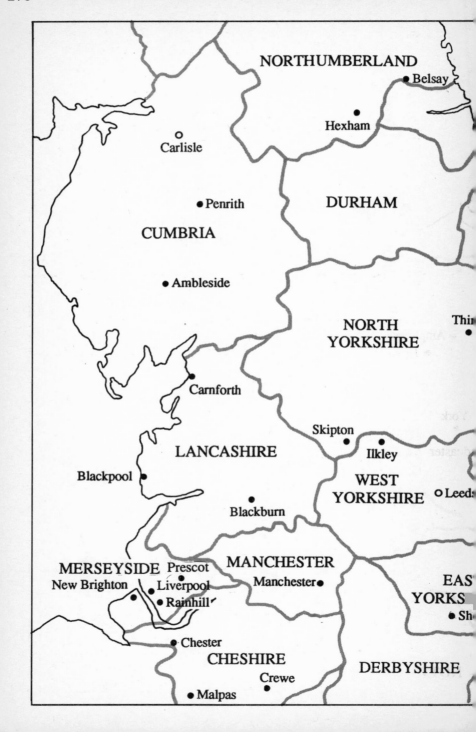

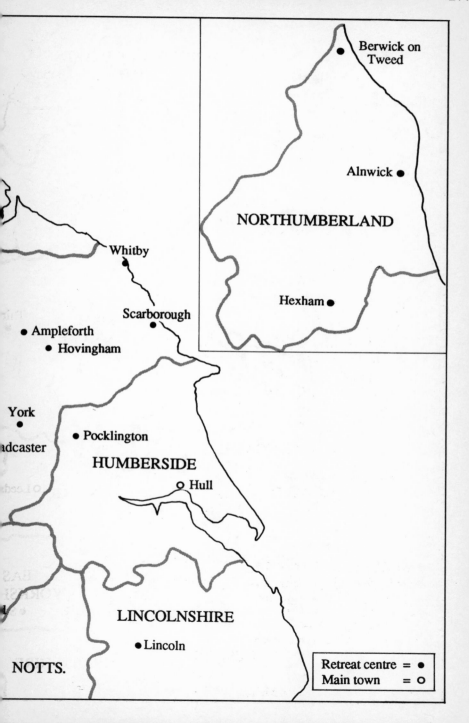

Berwick on Tweed

Alnwick

NORTHUMBERLAND

Hexham

Whitby

Scarborough

Ampleforth

Hovingham

York

Pocklington

adcaster

HUMBERSIDE

Hull

LINCOLNSHIRE

Lincoln

NOTTS.

Retreat centre = ●
Main town   = ○

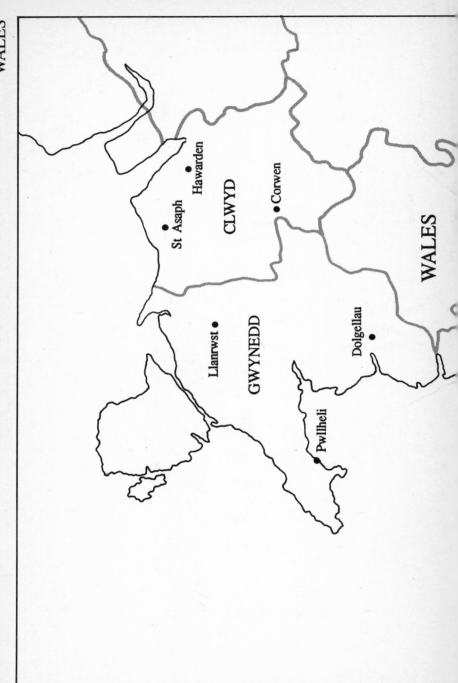

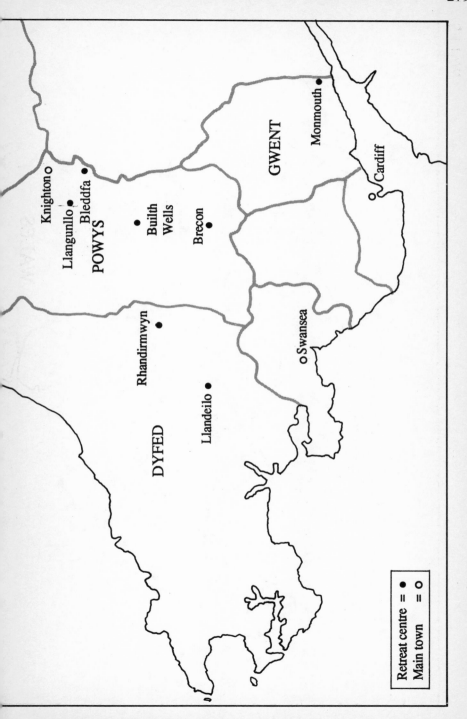

Knighton o

Bleddfa ●

Llangunllo ●

POWYS

Builth ●
Wells

Brecon ●

Rhandirmwyn ●

DYFED

Llandeilo ●

GWENT

Monmouth ●

Cardiff o

o Swansea

Retreat centre = ●
Main town = o

SCOTLAND

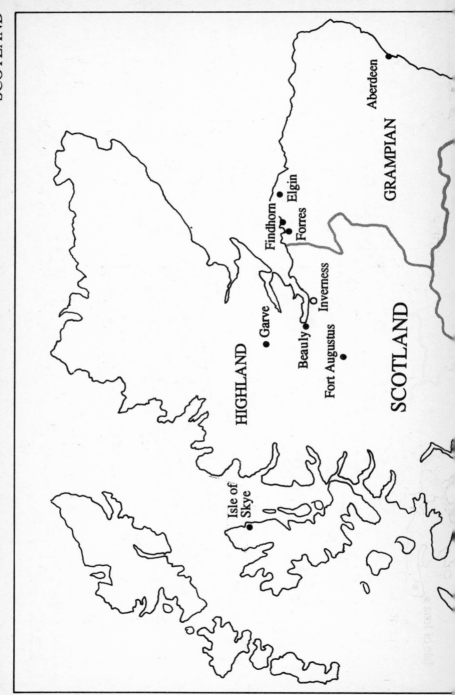

SCOTLAND

HIGHLAND

GRAMPIAN

Aberdeen

Elgin
Findhorn
Forres

Garve
Beauly
Inverness
Fort Augustus

Isle of
Skye

TAYSIDE

Crieff •
Perth •

CENTRAL

Dunblane •

Falkland •

Glasgow •
Largs •
Isle of Cumbrae

STRATHCLYDE

Haddington •
Musselburgh
Edinburgh •

LOTHIAN

Berwick on
Tweed
○

BORDERS

Hawick •

Langholm •

DUMFRIES AND
GALLOWAY

ENGLAND

Alnwick •

NORTHUMBERLAND

Isle of Iona •
Isle of Mull

| Retreat centre | = | ● |
| Main town | = | ○ |

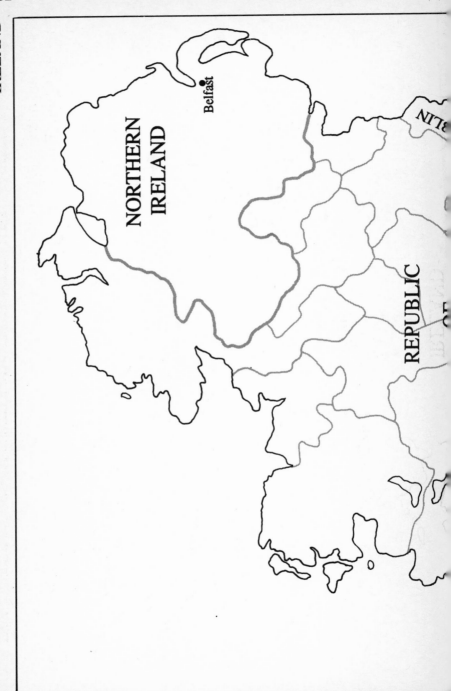

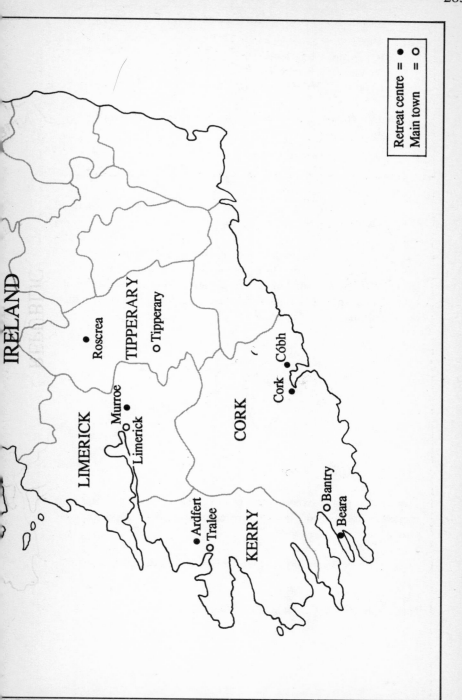

IRELAND

Retreat centre = ●
Main town   = ○

TIPPERARY
○ Tipperary
● Roscrea

LIMERICK
● Murroe
○ Limerick

CORK
Cork ● Cóbh

KERRY
● Ardfert
○ Tralee
○ Bantry
● Beara

To: The Good Retreat Guide
       Random Century House
       20 Vauxhall Bridge Road
       London SW1V 2SA

I visited the following retreat place on ----------------------- 19 ------

Establishment Name ---

Address --

Post Code ---------------------- Telephone ------------------------------

In the space below, please describe what the retreat was like and give any other details you feel to be relevant. For example, what you thought of the rooms and meals, the situation, atmosphere, spiritual help offered, special activities and charges. (Please continue on the reverse of this sheet, if necessary.)

From my personal experience I recommend this retreat centre for inclusion in/exclusion from future editions of *The Good Retreat Guide*.

I am not connected in any way with this retreat centre other than as a guest.

Name and address (BLOCK CAPITALS, PLEASE)

Signed ---